THE LITTLE
GOOD PEOPLE

❧ The LITTLE ❧
GOOD PEOPLE

Folk Tales of Ireland by
KATHLEEN FOYLE

With Illustrations by
PETER FRASER

FREDERICK WARNE & Cº Lᵀᴰ
London & New York

Printed in Great Britain

CONTENTS

ILLUSTRATIONS

[vii]

PREFACE

You come on it in the cool of the dawning, or at nightfall when the bats are flying and the old cummers lay by their knitting . . . Tir nan Og, fair land of promise and of gathered dreams. For some it lies no farther than the bend of the road; and there are others who must retrace their steps to glimpse it with longing through a weariness of years. But all travel by way of a sleeping wood.

The sun lingers warm there and the noontides are drowsy. And always there is bird-song and twilights sweeter than any twilights in the world. And when the moon shines silvered boughs bend down to silver blossoms; and there is dancing on the green spaces to the delicate music of fairy pipes. And at cock-crow the sound of a bugle call—very strong and clear.

Watch and you will see the fairy people come tripping on joyous feet in and out amongst the whiteness of the hawthorn glades. And if your ears be sharpened the click-clack of the crickets turns to the faraway tapping of the leprechaun's hammer. The wee, sly, cobbling leprechauns, who know where the red Danes hid their treasure chests, and who have their own stolen butter-crocks filled with fresh minted gold. A man hearing the leprechaun's hammer should creep and seize him unawares for then he will be given a ransom of gold. Only he must not lift his eyes from his prisoner till it be paid in full—else will he find his wealth changed to withered dry leaves and holes left in each pocket that can never be patched. Treading away softly down through the bracken dells you may light on a fairy tailor intent on his work—with his yard-stick and goose and spool of stout thread, his industrious bright needle flashing swift as a dragon-fly. Will he sew you a coat? Well indeed now he might. . . . But take care lest the wearing of it bring you discomfort. Woe be if the craftsman draw blood in the fitting for then you must be doomed to feel pin-pricks to the day of your dying—or go mismated through life; or be changed to curmudgeon.

The closed flowers nod on slender stems, dew-wet and languid in the green gloom; and the trees trip one another down the shadowy ridings. . . . Oak and elm; tall waving spruce and silken birch. The rowan-tree, *crann caorthainn* in the Gaelic, with its blood-red berry and the holly-bush that shines for Christmas Day. And when the breezes blow it is as if a hand struck the cords of a harp —deep and harmonious.

It is but a step from the Sleeping Wood to the magic glades of Tir nan Og, the Irish fairyland, where glad hearts find eternal youth, and where the Little Good People stay safe sheltered. From whence dead warriors and old majestic kings return once in every seven years on a May morning, to ride down through the mists of the dawn—while the sound of a bugle call wakes the slumbering echoes.

THE FAIRY COBBLER of KILLOWEN

THERE was once a wee leprechaun who lived in the Mourne mountains and he was as old as the hills. He wore a tall peaked hat on him; and he had a long white beard and eyes as blue as windflowers.

He cobbled the fairies' small buckled shoes and fashioned the clogs they were after wearing when it rained; and every morning in life he strolled down the brae the length of Killowen, to an old cummer who had a cabin by the road-side and supported herself by doing a bit of sprigging, to beg a sip of buttermilk and a piece of soda-bread. She never refused him, poor as she was, and he would thank her kindly and away with him up the hill again. Soon she would hear the tapping of his hammer and the sound of him whistling at his work; and it would be company like for her sitting on a stool at her door with her hooped linen, making the neat, small stitches and broidered dots.

Well one morning in springtime, when the whins were like spilled gold and the hawthorns sweet with knotted buds, he never came . . . neither could she catch sight nor sound of him for the whole of two days. So at the end of the second day, as evening threw long shadows on the mountains and the conies were frisking and playing themselves in the half-light, what did she do but set out to find him.

She followed a wee, fern-bordered path that wound ever higher and higher until it reached a hidden ledge of rock . . . and there in a hollow thatched over with bracken and dried heather didn't she come on her little friend. And mighty glad he was to see her! For he had pricked his thumb, and him busied with an elegant pair of dancing pumps, and hadn't he a whitlow and a hand swelled up the size of two. He was nearly astray in his head with the pain that was in it; but the old woman knew just what to do, for she was clever with herbs and the like of that. She gathered her simples and made a poultice for his

[2]

thumb to draw the anger away—and every day after she climbed the hill with his wee provision and saw to it that he kept his thumb happed up and his arm in a sling.

The children grew afeared to go near her

The leprechaun was greatly beholden to her, and when he got better he made her the dandiest pair of shoes in the whole county of Down.

They were of fine-grained leather, soft and supple and shaped to a nicety . . . and the neighbours could not make out how in the wide world

[3]

she came by them. But she promised the lepre-chaun never to let on herself, so no matter how folk quizzed sorra a one could come at the truth of it.

And with that it was given out she was a witch and the children grew afeared to go near her.

If a cow took sick, or a well ran dry, or the herring-boats had a poor catch, it was all put down to the Witch of Killowen. And times she came near to starvation and was lonesome want-ing the company of her neighbours. For no one would have any dealings with her or came now to caelie of an evening, when the fire on the hearth burned red and the rushlight glimmered in the corner.

Soon her eyes grew too dim for the close fine work; and she lost her wheen of hens; and was forced to put by her spinning-wheel for want of the flax.

And on a morning when the leprechaun came to her door says she to him, trembling:

"Your Honour, I haven't a piece in the house to give you . . . only a drink of fresh water that I am after drawing from the well and a few roots and berries that I gathered on the hillside. But indeed you are kindly welcome . . . If that will do you?"

[4]

PHELIM THE PIPER
Soon he heard the patter of dancing feet

The wee leprechaun looked at her strangely and seemed to ponder the matter in his mind.

"Hech aye, woman dear," says he, "and would you tell me why you starved yourself—you with a pitcher of butter-milk and grand wheaten farl beyont there on the dresser?"

And sure enough when she turned wasn't there a crusty brown farl sitting and it warm from the oven,

The wee leprechaun looked at her strangely

and the milk with the lumps of butter floating the way it does be coming straight from the churn.

"Take the shoes from off your feet," says the leprechaun, cutting short her acknowledgments,

[5]   B

"for I misdoubt me but I did you a bad turn in contriving a kindness. There are those that place obstacles in every man's path and must set themselves to be tripping all who walk straight! Maybe you might travel safer in your old brogues, agra, and I will leave you the price of my handiwork and bid you good-day."

At that he made his adieux and set off up the hill with the cummer's worn shoes trailed behind him by the strings. And he discontinued his visits from that on. But she found a gold-piece when she lifted her butter-crock and it kept her in comfort for many's a day.

And because she was a gentle old creature, with her charms and her cures, all foolish talk of the Evil Eye or the like of that died away at long last. People knew her again for an honest, harmless, poor woman, and would stop to pass the time of day or discuss how the rheumatics had them destroyed. Whilst the children strayed to her doorstep to share their small secrets and show their hid treasures and dandelion posies.

Up on the hillside the leprechaun hammered away. And long after the old woman was dead and gone the sound of his tapping could be heard, very brisk, as he shaped the dancing slippers for the fairies of Killowen.

PHELIM the PIPER

WHEN Phelim the blind piper played on his pipes there was a magic in his music. Lilting over the hills would sound the silver clamour of his reeds, and all the birds of the air would know to answer him. Throaty murmur of ring-dove and willow-warbler. Tinkling note of meadow-lark and wren. The liquid, lovely melodies of black-bird and thrush. "Sing with me, sing with me," the pipes of Phelim would plead, and from green branch and thicket the little, wild music-makers sang at his bidding. "Come, come," he would whistle, standing to listen for the small silken rustle of their flight. And tilting, clinging, sway-

[7]

ing, they came, spreading bright wings for him who had no eyes to see.

He had no mind pictures to beguile him in his darkened world, since he had walked sightless all his days, so music was his life and all of beauty in the sounds that came to him.

He knew the voice of the tall trees and of the whispering grasses, the changing songs of wind and wave. For him small, rippling streams told happy stories, and still-lake waters held a secret message. To him would come flowing the shy perfume of the flowers, the chime of the heather bells, the busy droning of the bees. Laughter of children was in his music and the stir of dancing feet. And sometimes it would be sad with the sorrow of one lamenting in desolate places. But mostly it was joyous, for Phelim the Piper had a light heart and many friends, and in all the wide province of Ulster was never the like of him to raise a tune at a wedding or a skirl at the cross-roads for the jigs and the merry-making.

Kind friends he had and those willing and able to minister to his comfort, but he loved best to roam contentedly, travelling the sweet roads of spring, the heather byways and the fallow fields.

No door but opened at his touch, and there was always the welcome of an inn or kindly shelter of some poor man's dwelling. Sitting by the hearth the small homely sounds of the house-place would come to him. Clatter of pails and plash of a churning. The purring of a kettle from its swinging crook and slow dunt of the cradle rockers on an earthen floor. And above the busy whirr of the wheel a woman's gentle voice to question.

"Is there a sadness on you the day, blind man, that you sit so silent and still in the shadows?"

"No sadness, I thank you, woman of the house, saving a regret that I may not see the kindness of your glance."

"Have you walked long in darkness, my poor fellow?"

"The whole of my life, indeed, woman dear, since the sight of my eyes was lost to me at birth. But sure there is always the music and a power to be dreaming!"

Small hands brought the wayside blossoms that he might discover each separate charm. Furry feel of wort and silverweed. The satin of daisy and curving buttercup. And as he stooped soft arms would cling about him and rounded cheeks be pressed against his own.

"How comes it that you cannot see us, tall man, when your eyes are wide open? Do you

[9]

not know that the fields are green and the flowers white and yellow? Is it dark night with you all the day long?"

And he would answer quickly, lest a child's joy be shadowed: "What need to see you, little friends, since I hold you in my heart! Your touch I know and your aery tread, and your voices that differ as pealing bells. Come now, and take me to where the blackbird builds her nest, and I will pipe you the proud song she sings when her eggs are all laid."

He must have been forty years of age, or maybe more, and him returning over the mountains from a wedding feast in the lowlands of Down, when the wonder of his life came upon him.

He had walked far and was tired, and so sat down on a mossy boulder to rest awhile. The full of the moon was at hand and though he could not see the white radiance of the night he sensed the clarity of the air and the stillness about him. His pipes lay idle across his knee, and there was no breath of the breeze to be singing to him, and yet there came stealing on his ear the sound of faint music differing from his own imaginings. Delicate music it was, yet harsh and discordant, being broken in its melody as if those who made it had no art. At first it was so strange and faraway that he mis-doubted his hearing, but as he listened it came nearer and it seemed that he sensed the rhythm of dancing feet—small, fairy feet, that fell light as thistledown. Then a soft voice spoke close to his ear, so that he started and put out his hand, only to close it on the empty air.

"Phelim the Piper," said the small voice coaxingly, "you that has the music of the reeds, will you be after playing for our dancing?" And Phelim must have granted a greater request for the charm of the pleading.

"'Deed and I will so," says he. "But who are you at all that knows my name and my powers, and if you be elf or fairy, how comes it that your own magic pipes are so shrill?"

"Man, dear," the wee, soft voice answered him despondently, "sure the musicians that we have at the present time were trained in a bog, and there isn't a note in their pipes but the far crying of the curlew and the lonesome whingeing of the wind. We have no wish to dishearten the poor things and them delighted to be obliging us, but our feet that should be tripping must tread a sad measure."

Phelim, ever-kindly, laughed then, and lifting his pipes made music that was lightsome as a

summer song. Soon he heard the patter of
dancing as the fairy folk surrounded him, the
whoops of them in a reel and the clapping of
their hands as they finished a set. All the old
country airs he played to them, and some born
sweetly out of the night's still magic and the
midsummer gladness. Reel and jig, gavotte and
roundel, and it seemed there was no weariness on
him more, nor shortness of breath, only a great
delight, and him playing blithely in the moonshine for the frolics of the fairy hosts upon the
green sward.

He heard faint breathings as though the wild
animals of the hills drew near to listen, treading
softly on their timid feet, and a little mountain
rill ran tinkling over its pebbles down to the valley
and the waiting sea, but there was no sound else
in all the sleeping world as he wove his melodies.

On and on he played until with the chill of the
dawn the spell of his music was broken, and he
knew himself to be alone. There fell on him then
a great languor so that the pipes slipped from his
grasp and he cast himself face downward on the
heather, his head striking a stone and a deep sleep
descending upon him.

Long hours passed over him lying there, and
when he came to himself the sun was high in the

heavens and the warm odour of opening flowers fragrant on the breeze. And waking, he was conscious of a shimmering mist where always there had been darkness and of dim shapes floating about him so that he cried out in fear, not knowing the wonder of his dawning power. His pipes lay where they had fallen and fingering them he drew comfort from their familiarity—peering to see dark gleam of ebony and sheen of silver stops.

Then rising with the sweat damp upon his brow, he stumbled down the hill a little way, and stood again as his vision cleared and the miracle of his recovered sight reached his understanding.

A wee shepherd lad came climbing the hillside, whistling to himself, and Phelim the Piper looked on the first living face that ever he saw.

"Dear little lad," he said, and his voice shook, "would you tell me where I am at all. Is it Tir nan Og I am in or Heaven itself, and me not conscious of death?" And he shaded his eyes from the glory of the sun.

The shepherd boy straddled his legs and laughed up from a round, merry countenance.

"Where are you," says he, "but on the heights above Carlingford on a June morning with Heaven no nearer than the top of Slieve Gullion; and will you cease making fun of me,

[13]

decent man, and me busy chasing my sheep."

He went whistling on his way then, and Phelim the Piper, who had been blind, stayed still to gaze.

Below him stretched the blue ribbon of the lough and steep fall of larch and pine woods mantling the slope of great hills; while all around lay the fertile downlands patched with

He shaded his eyes from the glory of the sun

green fields of rye and barley, with plains of pink clover and white bean blossom.

The shadows of the clouds went drifting slowly, and the gold of the gorse was a leaping flame that burned in the hollow places.

He watched the happy soaring of the birds and movement of life about him; the creeping of jewelled insects intent upon their secret purpose, the delicate marvel of a moth's spread wing. Wild bees hovered above the hanging spray of briar and honeysuckle and at his feet the little heath flowers wove a starry carpet—mountain daisy and harebell, thrift and sea-campion. And he trod that he might not crush one small, bright petal.

Long he stood at gaze savouring the sweetness of the gift restored to him before he raised his adoring face to the blue sky.

"Sure I never knew," said Phelim the Piper, "that the whole world was a wonderland for those having eyes to see!"

Fairy Gold

ONE morning, very early, when the sun sailed
 red and round,
Before the dews had lifted or the song-birds
 made a sound;
Across the glistening meadows, where the first
 lambs lay in fold,
Merry-legs, the fairy man, went seeking fairy
 gold.

A little brook ran purling, and he followed in
 its wake
To delve for burnished pebbles or largess from
 the brake:
A bunch of yellow catkins; some lichen chrome
 to shine;
He plucked a peeping primrose and a bud of
 celandine.

Dandelions and saffron-wort he added to his
    store;
But still there lacked full measure, and he cast
    about for more:
Here a pinch of daisy-dust, and now he made
    a sprint
To where the gilded buttercups gleamed like a
    fairy mint.

Busily the fairy man searched hillock, dell, and
    cove,
E'er honey-bees allured him to the moorland's
    treasure-trove;
Close-barbed, the lavish whin-flowers showed
    in glittering array
But he braved each doughty prickle and stole
    ransom gold away.

The
STONECUTTER'S ROAD

Down the road from where Tim Garvie lived
there was an old flint quarry, and whenever
school was over and Tim had no errands to run
for his mother he'd go there to play himself
amongst the heaps of chalk-whitened flints, and
about the ruins of the flint-knapper's working-
shed. The roof had fallen in and only one or
two grimy panes remained in the window-frame,
but it was a grand place to sport himself, and the
hut became a smuggler's cave or the stronghold
of Sorley Boy MacDonnell, just as the fancy
took him—for Tim Garvie had a great power of
dreaming.

One evening after a period of rainy weather he was scrambling over the hills and hollows and pools of water; and in a cave that was set among the earthworks and choked by a rank growth of nettles didn't he come on a strange, blackened, wee man, busy hammering and flaking at a pile of flints. First he quartered the stones and broke them in small slabs, and then he'd commence splitting again with blows from his hammer until he had a whole lot of arrow-shaped flints laid out in a row. It looked easy to do, and Tim, drawn by his interest, loitered nearer and nearer.

"Would you lend me your hammer 'till I see could I do that?" he asked the wee man, who looked up at him and smiled a queer, puckered smile.

Lifting a great flint in his two hands the knapper broke it into sections five to six inches in thickness, and then he bestowed his stone hammer on Timmy and signed to him to fire away. But Tim couldn't get the knack of it at all, and when he had finished his work the big flint lay pounded into useless shavings.

The knapper took back his tool and started his tap-tap, chip-chip, chink-chink, and Tim was free to study him in closer detail. He was a short, dark-featured wee man, with hair untrimmed and a cloak of skin thrown over his shoulders, and Tim had never clapped eyes on him before. " Do you come from these parts?" he asked, diffident about questioning but overcome by his curiosity. The wee man said " Aye," and just left it at that.

" I never mind to have seen you here before,"

Tim couldn't get the knack of it at all

said Tim, " and me playing in the quarry every day of my life. Are you going to mend the wee hut and start flint-knapping again?"

The stunted, wee man lifted his face and looked far away to where Ballygally Head reared itself

[20]

THE SLEEPING WOOD
" Well I know," said the little goose girl, " just who you are "

up against the gold of the sunset, and faintly in the silence left by his hammer came the sound of the tide churning noisily against the sea wall and the rocks.

"That's the Devil's Churn," said Tim Garvie, "and when there's a storm blowing no boat that was ever built could live in the turmoil of the waters, unless she'd be steel-plated and driven by steam."

"The Churn is known to me," said the knapper. "Death to the coracles is that pool of devils' water; but death for the raiders with flint-greed in their hearts who seek to enslave us by the might of their long spears. Not once, but many times have I seen the strand beleaguered, and the churned waters reddened by the blood of warring men."

Tim Garvie straddled his legs and looked long and hard at the blackened wee man.

"Sure that was long, long ago," he objected, "and you're not remembering to have seen it—only telling it out of history books."

The flint-knapper broke another stone, and re-started his clinking tune, tapping flint against flint and engaged now in the fashioning of a flat implement that had the shape of an axe.

"There's not one in the world," persisted Tim

Garvie, "who could look back to the days when they'd be taking weapons from the flint pits for the tribal wars. . . . But my schoolteacher can be telling of the days when men lived in holes in the earth and pile-dwellings, and came here to be making the axes and arrow-heads for their belts and bows."

Tap-tap, chip-chip, chink-chink, went the flint-knapper's hammer, and it seemed that the rain-washed quarry was strangely changed. The clumps of gorse and bracken groves were gone, and everywhere rose fresh piles of flint rubble, while short, dark-featured men and women worked with picks, scooping out the underground galleries in the chalk that before had appeared overgrown and more than half filled with earth.

With Tim Garvie staring as though he could scarcely believe his eyes the first little man touched him on the arm. "Come," he said, and moved amongst the busy hive of workers to take a rough and puddled footpad, high-banked and edged with coarse grass, that led from the quarry, and that was never used except by cattle, or for the carts that drew the loads of kelp up from the shore.

The wee man was talking to himself in an under-tone, and now seizing Tim Garvie by the hand he quickened his lope into a run.

"Let me go," said Tim. "I'm wanting away home to my mother, so I am, and I'm not knowing you or this way you have brought me at all —though the road we are on looks the same as our boreen, and there's the Ring Stone still set in our five-acre field."

The sight gave him confidence and he tried to pull the wee man towards it, but the flint-knapper only halted and considered, sniffing the air like a hound and keeping ever to a trail in the flattened mud that led to a ridge overlooking the quarry and the Devil's Churn. And gazing down to the strand Tim's breath almost forsook him at the things that he saw.

Long boats had grounded on the shingle and yellow-haired men were leaping ashore armed with battle-axe and spear, and splendid in glittering helmet and breastplate. They advanced along the stonecutter's road in a close knot, heading for the quarry, and glancing warily as though they feared they might be taken by surprise, and some in the centre, who seemed to be chiefs, had round shields and bore broad, flat swords.

Tim, all excitement now, would have plied his companion with questions, but the flint-knapper seemed to have forgotten him entirely. Stretched in the shadow of a great boulder he put fingers in his mouth and three times sounded the curlew's call, while from the distant quarry came a wavering note in answer. As if at a given signal Tim watched the squat workers scurrying like ants to reach a certain point from which they disappeared into the bowels of the earth, so that in no time at all there was nothing to see but the piles of flints and the rubble mounds.

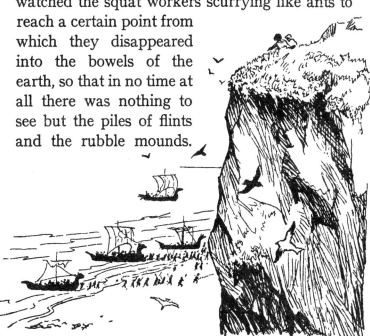

Yellow-haired men were leaping ashore

The knapper dropped his hands and grinned his queer, puckered grin.

"These tow-heads will take our flints," he grumbled, "but the knappers have gone to earth like foxes, and they will stay hid till the danger

[24]

is past. Not many flints will be found, because we have grown wise and bury as we make; and sometimes when the haul has been poor the pirates burn our homes. We are small in numbers and may not pit our strength against their long spears, so it is best to go to earth like the foxes and to be ready in sounding the curlew's call."

Tim Garvie, his eyes large with wonder, searched the twisting length of the stonecutter's road, and presently with a great tramping and shouting the raiders reappeared. Sacks that gave out a clinking sound were thrown over their shoulders, and as they rounded the last bend the guards left by the boats commenced to push the beached craft out into the surf.

Soon the sea-raiders were aboard, and the oars dipped to a gusty song as they sailed away over waves that were reddened by the flame of the setting sun.

"They seek a fresh goal," said the flint-knapper grimly, "and maybe on another shore there shall be clangour of blows and splitting of heads. But now we go back to the quarry to bring word that ears and noses are no longer in peril."

Pursuing his own fancies, Tim could not have told just when he missed the wee man—but there he was alone in the quarry with the dank rain pools glistening in the sunset, and long shadows resting on the empty hillocks and grass-grown piles of stones. No swarming droves of knappers came up from the earth, though he shouted his best, and he sought in vain for footprints or some proof that he had not been at the dreaming again.

Once he ran, sure that he heard the tap-tap, chip-chip of the knapper's hammer, but it was only a corn-crake mocking him from the five-acre field, and at last he had to go away home to his bed, mistrustful that maybe the whole of it had been make-believe. For by and large Tim Garvie had a great power of dreaming.

The Sleeping Wood

" I WONDER," said the little goose girl, bending
to gaze at herself in the pond on the common, " I
wonder now if I washed in May dew, and made
my curtsy to the new moon every time, could I
be helping myself to a wee knowin' of beauty?"

The grey gander, who had a spite at her,
stretched out his long neck and hissed in derision.
" Woman dear," he seemed to jibe, " will you take
a better look at yourself this minute!   At your
red head and powdering of freckles; and the nose
of you turning up when it should be small and
straight. . . .   Is it beauty!"   And he lowered

his head and sullied the shallows with his bill,
clouding the bright pool.

Just for that the little goose girl flung a clod
at the grey gander, making him dance angrily on
his webbed feet, and chased him with her cudgel,
demeaning him before his wives.
But then she laughed and forgot
her vexation in the gladness of

She knelt again and looked into the pond

the world about her. Then she knelt and looked
again into the pond.

Two finches were building in a blackthorn bush,
and she climbed a mossed bank to peep and see
their spotted eggs, and then must pluck a spray
of crab-apple bloom to deck her cudgel and crown
her red head. Now she crossed the common as

[28]

a queen, her robes of state trailing the ground
and her staid court streaming before, led by the
grey gander pacing pompously. With pointing
sceptre she swept beyond the confines of the
common down a grass-verged narrow lane where
her flock might scatter and feed—and, forgetting
her majesty, swung blithely on a creaking gate,
with the gander making short runs at her tattered
petticoats.

"I am thinking long," sighed the little goose
girl, teasing the gander with a bare brown toe,
"to get knowing what lies beyond there in the
Sleeping Wood. If I might leave the clatty geese
and go straying there by my lone there's no telling
what wondrous adventure mightn't befall me.
Maybe a prince would come riding down through
the glades on a white charger, with shining
armour and a red plume waving and him stooping
from his saddle to get lifting me up before
him. And when he kissed me I'd turn into a
whole beauty, fit to be queening it with the best,
and the two of us living happily for ever and
ever!"

The grey gander, with his round eye fixed
desirously on a field of young corn, made a dart
through the gate, and before the little goose girl
had emerged from her dreams his eight wives,

giving the password to the goslings, shook out their clipped wings and scuttled behind him.

"Dear, but I am heart-scalded by that old gander!" bemoaned the little goose girl. "For no one could watch him, so wily and wicked he is." And she went chasing between the green furrows with a concern for the frown of Farmer Donough if he should chance to sight such terrible trespassing and destruction.

"Will you come away out of that," she screamed, making a grab at the grey gander as he legged it towards a gap in the hedge—then they were all of them through the hole and past a wide margin of buttercups, lady's smocks and cuckoo flowers on the other side, headed straight for the secret enchantment of the Sleeping Wood.

Darkling firs and larches crowded, and the flocked geese moved silently over a close carpet of pine needles; and then tall beeches fanned to make a green gloom while everywhere the misted bluebells curtsied to the breeze. Now it was oak and hornbeam with the hawthorns of the under- growth white with bud and blossom; and here the holly bushes still kept their shining berries as it might be for Christmastide, though the chest- nut candles were lit and small woodland creatures gambolled at their May games.

The grey gander honked his discovery of a patch of goose grass, and the flock separated to go nibbling contentedly; but the wee lassie had forgotten them entirely and her wandering away bewitched down the green ridings, that might disclose at any moment some wondrous adventure.

Ah, it was lovely in the Sleeping Wood with the budding trees all around, and you with your secret thoughts flowering so that it seemed you held a posy in your hands! And in the middle of an ash grove, where the long sun rays fell slanting, the prince of her dreams came cantering on his snowy steed with shining armour and a red plume flaunted . . . Only when the dazzlement had gone from her eyes it turned out to be no more than Patrick Creegan, the miller's boy, on a shaggy donkey, and the both of them dusted white with mealies.

The Creegan boy pulled up with his long legs dangling, and he had freckles, too, and a plume of red hair sticking up on his head.

" Did you meet a cavalcade of horsemen going down the forest?" he questioned with a lordly air on him and his heels digging into the donkey's dusty flanks the way you might think that he boasted long spurs. " They rode in line, and go to prepare the castle against the time I'd get in

[31]

to be stripping off my harness. Brian Boru is
the name that is on me, and I'm just after fighting
a bout with the Danes."

"Well I know," said the little goose girl, "just
who you are. You're Patrick Creegan that runs
errands for the miller the same as I mind the
geese for Farmer Donough, so you needn't take
on yourself to be making up stories."

"Have you no power of dreaming?" asked the
miller's boy, and laughed with his wide mouth.
"Don't you know I can be anybody I like, and
me riding down through the Sleeping Wood on
a May morning. It could be Ecca of the Fleet
Horse, or Balor of the Blows, or John Courcy,
himself, from the castle beyont, and me riding to
conquer Ulster with a thousand men at my back.
Could you not let on yourself to be Grania or
Queen Maeve?"

"I don't know any of them ones," said the little
goose girl, "and I just let on to be waiting for a
fairy prince to come riding. But sure it's only
stories, and when I quit making-believe I'm just
Maggie Mulcahy minding the geese for the Farmer
Donough, and me homely and red-headed, and
not fortunate at all."

"It's lucky to be red-headed," the miller boy
bragged, "and if you're the seventh son of a

[32]

seventh son, like myself, you can't put a foot astray. Micky Hogan, the wee, black, cindery man who tends the underground fire at the mill, told me that, and said I'd go out to America and find prosperity. It was from him I heard about Brian Boru and Queen Maeve, and Balor of the Blows."

"If I ever found the leprechaun's gold," said the little goose girl, "I'd buy my mother a silk dress for Sunday, and my father a broadcloth coat like the Farmer Donough's. And I'd have shoes for myself with silver buckles on them."

The miller boy regaled himself with a feast of sorrel leaves and wagged his head knowingly. "If you came on the gold itself," he reasoned, "it mightn't be bringing you as much good as the money you'd work for with your own two hands. I'll get what I want in the long run, and I'll get it for myself and no thanks to the leprechauns."

High overhead the small birds sang bravely with a blackcap piper to be giving the note.

"I must go," said the little goose girl, "and 'tis certain I should be finding a new way back to the common, for I daren't let the geese next or near the young corn."

"I'll show you a short cut out on to the road," said the miller boy, "and then I'll be parting from you. Though we'll be meeting again some day in the Sleeping Wood."

When the little goose girl had gathered her flock, and they had passed out beyond the flowery margin of the spinney, the miller boy dug in his heels and urged his shaggy mount to a jog-trot.

" So long," shouted the miller boy, smiling with his wide mouth and shaking back the red plume of his hair.

"So long," shouted the miller boy

" So long, Patrick Creegan," the little goose girl called softly, and stood a long time to wave and watch him riding away from her down the bright road.

[34]

LINT
IN THE
BELL

LONG ago in the olden times when Ulster farmers all grew and scutched their own flax, and when you would hear in every cabin the brisk birr of the wheel, and see on the bleach greens the long lengths of white linen spread like snow in summer, there lived not far from the town of Lisburn a journeyman weaver by the name of John Connor.

He travelled the country the whole year round, visiting the different homesteads and weaving the spun yarn for the factor's or the housewife's own use; and because he was well liked, with a cheering smile and ready hand for the world, everyone welcomed the loom-man, as he was called, and made much of his coming.

Setting up his rough frame in loft or outhouse he would labour diligently at his weaving as long as daylight lasted, but at nightfall when the men

had come in from the fields and the family
gathered round the fire, he sat joining in their
crack or nursing the little ones before they were
sent away to bed. And many's the tale he could
tell of gnomes and fairies, and of the cobbling

Many's the tale he could tell of gnomes and fairies

leprechauns that lived in the Mourne Mountains,
each with a hidden crock of goblin gold.

With the children held fast in a spell of wonder,
the womenfolk would lay their heads together
and make plans, saying amongst themselves that
it was a pity and a shame to see such a well-
favoured, thrifty fellow living by his lone; but still
the Weaver travelled cheerily on his industrious

pilgrimages, seemingly well contented with his lot.

Once on a day he went journeying through the midsummer meadows and fields that held the tender hue of lint in the bell, and overtaking a brown peddling woman stopped to shoulder her pack.

"Good-morrow to you, decent man," said she. "And does your own load sit so light that you are fit to be lifting a stranger's burden?" And she glanced up at him pleasantly from under the cowl of her shawl, and stepped out bravely beside him on the dusty road, glad of his goodwill and company.

A very small brown woman she was, with a criss-cross of wrinkles and eyes as black as sloes, planning to tramp the Ards and winding coast ways peddling her wares. Bits of fine lace and needlework for the gentlefolk, with trinkets and combs and coarse wearing stuffs to tempt farm lassie and fisherman's wife. When the time came for her to be parting company with the Weaver she sorted through the tangle in her pack, and would have pressed some pretty thing upon him "for the one of his heart."

"I have neither sweetheart nor wife," replied the Weaver, "so put up your geegaws, woman

D

dear. But I'll take a good wish for the road and be thanking you kindly."

"May your road be lucky," said the small peddling woman, "and may your love, that is as lint in the bell, make a trusty warp with a weft of sweetness."

And she nodded her head at him and went padding away between the flowery hedge-rows and fields clouded blue with flax in blossom.

The Weaver, making good speed towards his destination, reached a certain neat steading soon after sundown. As he turned the last bend of his road a round moon cleared the hills and there sounded a rustling in the summer leaves as if some green-clad pixie had him ambushed; while presently the hedge shadows disclosed a six-year-old girleen with dancing eyes and a mouth that smiled.

"Marget, agra, and is it yourself that's in it?" marvelled the Weaver, letting on to be all astonishment, "and me mistaking you for a fairy strayed beyond the green ring to put a spell on me so that I'd lose my heart."

The lassie laughed out at that, and smoothed her gown with a small sedateness.

"Sure I'm waiting on you this long time," she

[38]

made answer, "since I knew you were to come to
our house when my mother swept the left-over
apples from about the weaving frame, and bade
my father carry the spun yarn up to the loft. She

The hedge shadows disclosed a six-year-old girleen

gives me leave to be serving your stirabout; and
I won't sleep a wink till I hear again how the King
of the Northern Fairies put his come-hither on
the turfcutter's daughter."

"Come hither to me," cajoled the Weaver, and

[39]

set his arms about her to take her safe home.

Each day of his weaving she sat by his loom
with her eyes intent for the even crossing of warp
and weft, and a waiting smile whenever he raised
his head; and often her voice, that had a bird's
singing note, sounded high above the click-clack
of the treadles and thud of the batten.

For her delight he created a magical world
where they went wandering together, and no one
must know the sweet secrets they shared or hear
the fantasies that he strung for her in the firelit
shadows, whispering of the wee white house,
brown-thatched and starry-paned, that the fairies
planned to be building for her when they got
time; and of how they had plucked the blue flax
flowers that were her eyes, and spun the bright
threads of her hair, so he might weave them a
cloth of gold.

He made her a wheel, so neat and deftly
fashioned that it might have fitted an elfin good-
wife, and guided her small fingers in the use of
the distaff; while her first spun yarn was made
into wristbands for his wearing, with the careful
stitches exact and straight.

Before he knew, her childhood had passed and
he loved her as a woman, with a faint-hearted

despondency for the score of years that lay now like a barrier between them.

"You *omadhaun*," he chided himself, "would you ask to tie the sweet youth of her to an ageing man? Let you be leaving her for some fine young fellow fit to bring a poetry along with his wooing; and take care now that no word from you dims the joy that will be coming to her." And in an effort to ease the hunger of his heart he cut adrift and absented himself for a twelve-month and more, having got apprenticed to a Quaker merchant of Dunmurry who could be teaching him the wool-weaving and small niceties of his trade. Not a housewife up and down the country but hadn't a sore lament for his departure, and the cobblestones of Lisburn missed the firm ring of his feet.

Lint was in the bell when he returned to his own neighbourhood and sought out the lassie in her home.

She was alone in the houseplace and busied at her wheel, with the door set wide to the freshness of the air, and late afternoon sunshine patching the kitchen walls and quarries. And as she turned and treadled words that she sang floated outby to the listening Weaver.

Now when the hearth is swept and clean,
And gently glows the kindly peat,
I sit my polished wheel beside
The flying treadle 'neath my feet.

Turn, turn, my pretty wheel
And spin me now, I pray,
Fine thread that my true love shall weave
Against our wedding day.

The dancing light like moted gold
Falls on dark beam and dresser delf,
From sooted crane the kettle swings,
Sleek drowsy puss purrs to herself.

Turn, turn my pretty wheel
And my sweet fortune tell:
Will bridal gown be wove for me
From lint that's in the bell?

The Weaver stood in the doorway and she rose up to stretch out glad hands to him, as though he had come at the bidding of her heart. But then she set a chair for him and stayed with a width of the quarries between, fingering her stilled wheel.

"Marget," said the Weaver with the mastery of a man enchanted, "say that you love me the way I am loving you. Ah, darling of my heart, will there be a bride-spinning and happy weaving to be done from lint that's in the bell?"

She stayed mute and still for a moment's space,

and then she laughed softly and smoothed her gown.

"Dear John," she answered, "sure I'm waiting on you this long time, and loving you since the days when you told how the King of the Northern Fairies put his come-hither on the turf-cutter's daughter. And maybe, as you seem so slow at your work, John, you should be putting the weaving in hand without further delay—for indeed and indeed there is enough yarn spun."

Her eyes danced and her mouth was smiling and the Weaver took a quick step across the floor.

"Come hither," commanded the Weaver, and set his arms about her to take her safe home.

[43]

THE CHANGELING

MID the lone mountains of Donegal, at the time of the fairies, there lived a young farmer, McMichael, and his wife Bridgeen. Poor they were in worldly goods, with but a few sparse acres of stony land and a wee white house built into the bleak hillside, but they had riches in their health and strength and fondness for each other.

When their first babe was born it seemed that the whole of life's joy and wonder lay shrined and cradled with him—and indeed he was beautiful, this child of their love. Straight and sturdy of limb; milk-white and golden as his own birthmonth of May; with eyes that were blue as the skies of spring.

Bridgeen would sit dandling him at the door or carry him laughing to the fields where the father worked; and often she left him lying folded in her shawl among the flowery swathes of mown grass or yellow corn stooks while she lent her young energy to the harvest labours.

[44]

Haytime passed and corn-gathering and it was on her mind that the child had not been christened, but they waited for the coming of the grandparents from Inishowen and for the throng of the year's work to be over them. He was to

She left him lying in her shawl

be called Michael John after father and grandfather, and so Bridgeen named him endearingly as busied about her home affairs she talked and sang to him, or rocked the neat new cradle that had been so proudly fashioned and carved. And as she fetched and carried for the live-stock or

[45]

sat at her spinning she would play small childish games—hiding that his baby eyes might search for her and chanting a nonsense rhyme of her own blithe making:

> " Michael John, Michael John,
> Where can my sweet babe be gone?
> Peep and smile, so I see
> A wee son come back to me."

And the boy would kick and crow, feeling his lusty strength, never fretful or ailing—the dear pride and joy of her heart.

It happened one evening in late autumn that she went to the well, some little distance from the house, to draw her spring water and was detained longer than she had expected by a straying heifer. She hastened home, fearing that the child, left sleeping, might have wakened and be crying for her; but there was no sound in the houseplace as she set down her brimming pails and crept over to the cradle. The dusk was falling and only the red glowing of the hearth-fire lit the gathering shadows, but with the sudden flaming of a smouldering log she glimpsed the face of the thing that lay pillowed, and the frantic cries of her brought the home-coming husband running in fear. He found her stretched senseless on the

floor and it was not until the rushlight glimmered
that his startled gaze fell on the crib and he discovered the cause of her distress. For instead
of their own strong, beautiful boy was a strange
puny changeling, with staring vacant eyes and
slavering mouth—a thing that puled and whim-
pered, turning from the light, and beating the air
with claw-like feeble hands. Ill-nourished fairy-
child left by the wee folk, who had stolen Michael
John away!

Placing his unconscious wife upon the bed he
left her while he sought help and soon the house
was thronged by weeping women and neighbours
come to condole with them in their trouble.

Poor Bridgeen, roused to her sorrow, could only
tremble and moan, and seemed like to die of her
affliction. The intruder was hurried away and
kept from her lest the sight of it should drive her
to distraction; and in the weeks that followed she
came to be strangely altered—sitting listlessly
with folded idle hands or, more often, roaming
the hills by day and night searching and crying
for her lost darling. The poor young husband
keeping her company or striving to comfort her
grief, distraught and heart-broken as she.

People would shudder and stop their ears at
the sound of her chanting on her wanderings, the

[47]

thin thread of her song rising on the wintry air
with the wailing of the wind:

> " Michael John, Michael John,
> Where can my sweet babe be gone?
> Peep and smile, so I see
> A wee son come back to me."

It was a distant relative, anxious to minister to
them in their misfortune, who heard of an ancient
Wise Woman from beyond Killybegs, said to have
had dealings with the little people and to be well-
versed in the knowledge of spells and enchant-
ments. Word having been sent, craving her help,
she came travelling over the hills, her long red
cloak making a brave splash of colour against
grey landscape and snowy height, and with her
appearance at the door the first hope and gleam
of joy entered the stricken home.

They must fetch the fairy child to the house, she
said, and foster it for a year and a day; and at
the end of that time, when it was fat and well-
cared, they were to carry it at midnight to some
place frequented by the fairies and there leave
it, stark naked, at the mercy of the winter cold.
When the wee people came to nurture it, Michael
John should accompany them, and it might well
be that if the elf-child were taken the other would

[48]

be left. No kindness shown to the changeling would go unrewarded, but any neglect would be visited on the child of their love—and this threat the Wise Woman stressed the way poor Bridgeen might find it in her heart to mother the monstrosity.

For the whole length of the time decreed the goblin-child was nourished and fed—waxing fat and strong, so that the foster parents had their work set to supply its hungry needs. It cut teeth ; and would lie laughing foolishly to itself, but spoke no word nor seemed to recognize those who tended it—excepting that now and then it might catch Bridgeen's apron, and her passing the cradle, as if it had some wee love for her in its cold heart.

At long last the day of their deliverance was at hand, and in the lone watches of the night they carried their charge away to a green place where the fairies had been seen to dance and sport themselves on the short grass and spreading mosses. The way was brightly moonlit, with hoar-frost spangling each dewy twig and myrtle stem, and deep pools gleamed ice-bound and glittering in the shadow of tall-standing rush and leafless thorn. Bridgeen, in her tenderness, felt a pity for the helpless creature to be so cruelly exposed

[49]

and left a victim to the weather—but the Wise
Woman's commands must be obeyed, so un-
wrapping the child from the warmth of her cloak
she laid it down in the centre of a wide ring
that showed clearly-formed on the marshy plain.

The wee people came trooping merrily

Then hiding themselves behind some whins, and
in the shade of a rowan tree the way they might
escape enchantment, they waited for the midnight
hour.

Suddenly a strange mystic glowing seemed to
come from the earth itself and the fairy circle was

[50]

outlined in rainbow hues; while above the whimpering of the elf-child they heard a magic music that was like the singing of silver flutes and far-away chiming of small golden bells. Nearer and nearer, with the light growing stronger, until now the wee people came trooping merrily. Green clad and russet coated. High-peaked hat and buckled shoe. Hobgoblin and tiny troll, swinging and side-stepping in time to the lovely music that went rising and falling with the soft sighing of the autumn breeze. And then they were crowding and pressing about the naked babe while the light dimmed and the full moon was clouded for a passing space. The music faded, fainter and fainter, the dancing shadows were no more—and clear on the silence rose the full-throated lusty crying of a weaned and mortal child. Trembling and stumbling in eager haste, the young couple ran towards the sound, to discover their own loved Michael John safe brought and restored to them!

With feet scarce touching the ground, and eyes that vied with the stars in their shining, Bridgeen bore him home to where lit pane and expectant friend awaited their return.

Down between the sleeping hills, treading a silver pathway, safe sheltered by her husband's arm, the drowsy boy close gathered to her heart. And neighbours heard her singing as she passed :

> " Michael John, Michael John,
> Here's my brave babe that was gone.
> Peep and smile, for you see
> A wee son come back to me."

Never so joyous a christening or such an out-pouring of love as welcomed the recovered child. And he grew to be a fine good man, with no mark of the fairy world upon him. One of many children; pride and solace of his parents until their lives' end.

DAN RUSSEL AND THE LITTLE RED MAN
As they roamed he would peer restlessly this way and that

Cat's-Cradle

At nightfall when the fire burns low
And crooked shadows spread,
Before my mother minds to say
That I should be in bed,
Larry beg, the leprechaun,
Steals from his secret nook
To sit and play cat's-cradle
With no one there to look.

Should I be clumsy and all thumbs
Unravelling a strand,
Larry beg, the leprechaun,
Just takes the thing in hand;
'Tis he shows fit to pull the strings
That ease the matter through,
For he's skilfully contriving
And queer an' friendly, too.

E

When I grow up to be a man
If things will not go right,
I'll think of playing cat's-cradle
With Larry beg at night
Of how he'd always persevere
To sort the tangled skein,
And maybe I'll be trusting him
To do the same again.

DAN RUSSEL
and the Little Red Man

DAN RUSSEL was the name the country people put on him because he was small and red-headed and cunning as a fox.

He had another plain, decent name that the poor-house authorities gave to him when he was found wandering the roads as a wee thing, having fallen from some tinker's cart and they not troubling themselves to look for him. But, like the trade that was taught him and the clothes provided, the name was a misfit; so that he came to be known always as Danny, or The Fox—which in the Gaelic is *O'Sionnach*. Poacher and trickster; crafty where there was no need for guile, trusting no man, and at the latter end with every man's hand against him, so he took to the woods. Living by the help of his traps and snares, outlawed and avoided for the evil that was in him.

Even the dogs, those friendly beasts, had no love for him, which is ever a bad sign on a man. The gentle guardians of farmhouse and barnyard would rise and snarl at his step, refusing to be pacified, while the rough curs of road and ditch stood with bared teeth and stiffened hair until kicked or stoned into submission. He never had but one dog to stay with him—an ill-humoured lean vixen that snapped at his heels and followed him with a grudging loyalty.

There was no laughter in him or kindliness, or the desire to mix with his fellows. Such pleasures as he knew he enjoyed secretly and alone; and he was ruthless in all his dealings as the wild creatures of tooth and claw he hunted and ensnared—obedient only to their laws of fear and hunger. In him was that wanderlust which sometimes drove him to join a gipsy tribe or tinker family roaming to far countries, but always he returned—seeking the places and wastes that he best knew, as a beast finds its way back to lair and burrow.

Now he would pitch his rude tent deep in the sheltering woods, within easy reach of grouse covert and game enclosure, now by some mountain lake or broad stream where the silver cock salmon came journeying down from the salt sea and the speckled trout slept in the shallows. But there was no love in him for the long play with rod and line—no sportsman's ardour of the chase. Sweeter to him the scream of a trapped rabbit in the bracken glades and all the stealthy approach and mean methods of the born poacher. The quick hand that clasped and choked—the cunning that must outwit and destroy.

It happened one day, as he knelt in a spinney fixing his wires, that he looked up to find a strange little man in a russet coat perched, straddle-legged, on the fallen trunk of a tree, regarding him intently.

He was a queer-looking wee fellow, with a sallow mask-shaped face on him and hair as tawny as Dan Russel's own, wearing a close skull-cap pressed down to his ears, which rose sharp and pointed on either side, and his eyes were sly and slanting as those of a cat.

He grinned at Danny, and the dog, that had stood growling and shivering since first it sighted him, took to its heels and made off, heedless of all whistling and imprecations, followed by a shower of fir-cones which the little red man sent

[57]

after it with the best will in the world. This roused Danny's anger so that he bent to retrieve knife and pliers, muttering savagely, while the stranger started to placate him.

He was a queer-looking wee fellow

"Och now, don't put yourself out," says he, in a high thin voice. "Sure I have no liking for dogs, good or bad, and we are as well wanting

[58]

that whelp, with neither courage nor pedigree; but stay you, Dan Russel, since I have things to say it might be worth your while to be hearing."

"Troth, and I will not detain you," replied Danny, still angered, "for by all the powers of darkness I want no truck or chat with the likes of you." And with that he turned as if to be going. But the little red man slid to the ground and intercepted him, standing in his path with legs set wide apart and arms akimbo, bright crafty gaze fixed keen and steady.

"Harken, now," he coaxed, "and don't be doing anything in a hurry that you will regret in aftertime. I have a great respect for you, Dan Russel, and have watched and waited this long while until we could converse. For, clever as you are at the poaching (and a neater hand I never saw on a man!) it's myself has the grand art of it entirely, and I was wishful to make it a partnership," says he.

Danny, not being well used to flattery, was surly and suspicious at first, but soon under the spell of the wee man's soft tongue and sly cajolery, he started to brag and boast on his own account, backing himself against any trickster in Ulster to tickle a trout or land a big springer, in and out of season.

[59]

The little red man professed a high regard for
Danny's powers, but was disdainful, it seemed, of
such an abuse of them. Fish, he opinioned, was
only palatable for the want of something better
and a waste of both skill and appetite. Game was
the thing, and, better again, a prime goose or fat
chicken, fresh from the barnyard. He smacked
his lips and rolled up his eyes so that now it was
Danny's turn to grin sourly.

"Bedad," says he, "with your help I might
soon be seeing the inside of the County jail. Will
you go away out of that, you thieving wee rascal,
and leave me to the management of my own concerns." At this he was for departing in good
earnest, but the little red man had still more to
say.

He proposed, on account of his size and agility,
to clamber into the hen-roosts at night while
Danny waited at a safe distance until he could be
helping away with the spoils. All the wee man
asked was a share in the bag and the doubt-
ful pleasure of Dan's company, for which he
appeared to have taken some sort of a strange
fancy. After much ill-humoured demurring on
the poacher's part, so it came to be arranged, with
them planning to meet at midnight near the same
spot.

The depredations of those two rapscallions would fill a whole book in the telling! There wasn't a hen-roost or flock of geese within miles safe from the pair of them, and at the first scent of

The depredations of the two rapscallions would fill a book

trap or danger they would be gone like the wind.

Oh, the fine stealthy hunting in the dusk, or on a winter's eve when the moon rode high and shadows lay long and deep. While the hoar-frost glinted on road and barn roof and the farmer waited with primed shotgun in a lonesome vigil. Plump Michaelmas goose seized and lifted e'er it could drop a leg from under it, with never a squawk, or fluttering of white feather to mark the trail. A fowl-house robbed and the drowsy birds pulled down from the perches before the rooster had opened sleepy eye to sound his raucous alarm, or watch-dog raised keen nose from passive paw. Oh, a light hand and smart foot had the little red man!

Grand times for Danny, the rogue, with pot always well plenished and money to jingle in his tattered pockets. But the end of it all came sure and swiftly.

After a while it seemed that the little red man grew less confident in himself, taking great pains to disguise their plans and change each meeting-place, as if to circumvent some secret and attentive foe. As they roamed he would peer restlessly this way and that, mindful of some terror and mystery surrounding them, and he had a trick of disappearing from Dan's side at so much as the rustle of a leaf or slight fall of a beechnut in the stillness. Danny mocked at him for being so jumpy and ridiculed all his wiles and evasions; but the little man continued to walk warily, with ever a backward glance for things that might be.

One night they set out for an adjacent farm to complete the plundering that had deprived a good-wife of half her laying pullets; but on reaching the moonlit haggard Dan Russel saw that which put a great fear into him. Forming a wide circle, with the scent of them heavy on the air and eyes luminous in the darkness, sat a whole gathering of foxes, waiting, so it seemed, motionless and intent. The little troll had sighted them, too, and with one hoarse cry he was through a whin gap, winging away like a dumbledore! Closely following, and noiseless in the shadows, padded the tawny pack, each flaunting brush laid flat and streaming on the wind—with Dan Russel, himself, at the tail of the hunt, dragged on against his will.

By moor and bog-road, where the jacksnipe rose in jagged flight and small prowling night things scurried and fled, or, cowering bright-eyed and timorous, peeped from dense oakling scrub and bramble fastness. Where the dark pools gleamed evilly in the crackling stubble of the heather and the stacked turf showed, ghostly and bedewed, under the waning stars. Past sleeping cabin and dim boreen, lone farmstead and shadowed rickyard. Away, away, over frosty meadow, fallow ridge, dank ditch and crumbling stone. Skirting the mere with its sodden banks and standing rushes, out towards the bleak marshlands and blackened heath, where the ragged rocks lay strewn amongst the smouldering gorse-fires and hidden burns murmured together, threading the silvered moss and short rimed grasses. Once a hare started and speeded with them, and once the pied badger, slinking stealthily, before it went to earth; while ever ahead streaked the small red quarry, lost and shrouded in the moving phantom of the mist or clearly descried beneath a full moon's brightness, the soundless vengeful host pressing hard upon his heels. Bats skimmed above them in the half-light with a soft whirr of leathern wings; and at the first glimmer of a cold dawn owls screeched plaintively from tangled thicket, answering the wavering note of curlew and peewit.

But now a strange unaccountable thing came to pass and fox hunted fox!

Where the red droich had been a bedraggled beast turned and twisted in search of shelter—striving to outwit the pursuing malice and cruelty of its fellows. Even as Dan Russel caught up with them, breathless and bemired, there was a sudden closing and swarming; he saw a limp and mangled form bandied and tossed high; heard a fierce snarling, awesome and tormented—then knew no more for the sickness and dread that fell on him.

When reason returned it was broad daylight and the warmth of a wintry sun thawing his frozen limbs. He dragged himself away into the woods and made to kindle a fire and heat his pot; but soon a horror of all solitary places oppressed him so that he deserted his old haunts—seeking the company of decent folk and asking, for the first time, to earn an honest living.

Three generations knew Dan Russel, for he reached a great age and came to be in good repute as a clogger and basket-weaver; but only to one old crony did he ever tell this strange story of the little red man and it was repeated long years after round the countryside as a wild uncanny tale, passing all belief.

The Fairy Tinker of Tyrella

LONG ago in the faraway days when you couldn't travel an Irish road without meeting a fairy— good or bad—there lived amongst the sand-dunes at Tyrella in the northern county of Down, a fairy tinker, or maybe a gnome, for he was a sizeable lump of a wee man and taller than fairies mostly are.

He made and mended the wee people's pans and griddles, and their pots that were no larger than a cockle shell, and from morn till night you would be hearing the clinking of his hammer and see the red glow of his fire that he fed with dried dune grass and bits of drift-wood from the shore.

He was clever at his work and brisk as a bee but with a queer, crabbed temper, and folk were always anxious to humour him because of the spite he might take at them if annoyed.

A sharp rap from his hammer would light on the knuckles of any mortal who tried to hurry him or ventured to dispute the price he asked for his repairs, and where the hammer struck there would be rheumatic pains and swellings that put them in mind of his displeasure for many the long day to come.

Should the fishermen refuse him a chew of tobacco or a piece of tarpaulin to shelter him from the wind they would find their lines tangled and nets full of holes, or the boats loosed from the moorings and drifting with the tide.

And maybe their luck would turn from them so that the catches would be poor and the seas contrary.

The wee tinker came to be greatly respected and not a fish-wife but would leave him a drink of goat's milk or a fresh wheaten farl when she had finished her baking, or maybe a herring, and her coming up from the boats with her creels.

But, behold you, this wasn't enough for him and in time he took to thieving.

At first it was only an egg now and then from the hen-roosts, or the fill of a pipe from some fisherman's pouch left lying with his coat on the shingle, but before long there wasn't a chicken safe from his pot or a place where he wouldn't be picking and stealing.

People were just heart scalded with his depredations—the wee black tinker that he was, and the mischief in him! But nobody could think of a cure that wasn't likely to recoil on the sufferer. And it would have taken you to have eyes at the back of your head in order to watch him.

There was one bright spring morning that a decent good-wife hung out her fine new feather bolster to air in the sun. And no sooner was she back in the house than happening to look through the window, she saw it whisked off the whin bush and the flash of a red-tasselled cap as my brave tinker made away with it.

She knew better than to set chase after him through the sandhills, and her the mother of a family with the breath getting short on her, but by and by, when she had the worst of her anger over her, she took her heather besom out of the chimney corner and set out for his wee encampment. And there, sure enough, was my bold imp sitting tinkering in the greatest ease comfortably perched on her best feathers! She couldn't find words at first, being overcome by his audacity, and then:

DAN RUSSEL AND THE LITTLE RED MAN
The farmer waited with primed shotgun

" I see you are saving your breeks—or is it your bones that need a bolster between them and the shingles?" says she.

She knew better than to set chase after him

The wee tinker never let on himself. He was busy riveting a neat handle on a tin lid, very exact, and he might have been stone deaf and as blind as a bat the way he disregarded her, besom and all!

[69]   F

But she saw the glint of his wicked bright eye and he brought his hammer down very vicious.

However, she had a great courage and the sight of her good bolster doubled up underneath his shins was more than she could bear, so she took a hold on herself.

"I'll thank you for the return of my bolster," says she. "Did I fill it with my best goose-down and sew my own spun linen for the likes of you to ease yourself on? Get off it this instant minute," says she, "for have it I will." And with that she made a sweep with her besom that scattered the sparks of the fire like flying stars, and tumbled the wee tinker into a pother of dried seaweed with his tin lid sounding on the pebbles like the clapping of cymbals.

He got up with his rage as white hot as his own soldering-iron, but before he could draw his breath the good-wife lifted the bolster and made off, never stopping until she reached her own door and had the bolts and bars drawn against him.

She let her burden down on the settle, and when her heart had ceased pounding, she began to feel pleased with the way things had turned out. "I have my bolster anyway," says she, taking it up to plim the feathers and near bruising the toes

off herself as she let it fall. When she ripped a
seam, wasn't it filled with sharp sand and small
stones, and there she let it lie until she had her
cry out. But after she had to laugh, thinking of
the angry trick the wee tinker had played her,
and of the fine tale she would have to tell. It
was no good trying to get the better of him and
people bore with his pranks, for they were all
afeared that he would ill-wish them or bring
worse trouble on anyone courageous enough to
cross him.

Well after a while it was noticed that he
absented himself from his usual haunts about
the shore, and he got very secret like and seemed
to want to be by his lone, chasing the children if
they stopped beside his fire and jouking down
among the dunes if the fisherfolk came in sight.

He had never been what you might call good
company, and if he was chatty you kept one hand
in your pocket and the other on your clasp-knife
or any small thing worth the lifting—but now he
was as sharp as a briar and as wicked as a weasel,
so that between his bad tongue and thieving ways
nobody fashed if he kept to himself. And then
he took to going away for long lengths of time
and people would live in hopes that it was for
good and all, and that maybe he would pitch his

tent in the harbour-town farther along the coast, where the picking might be better with the strange sailors coming off the herring-boats and them with their pockets full of big silver money. The fowls would get fat and there would be no scarcity of new-laid eggs. And the goats came home at night with their full yield of milk. All would be peace at Tyrella until one unlucky morn when the kindling wood left overnight disappeared from some good-wife's hearth, and there would be a clattering and commotion among the hens, and a roar as some pouch was found empty, telling all and sundry that the rogue tinker had returned.

Clink, clink, clinkerty clink, would go the sound of his hammer down amongst the sand-dunes, and there would be a curl of blue smoke rising from his cutty-clay filled with ill-gotten baccy, and the shrill voice of him raised in an argument.

Far along the strand rose one small hillock set with twisted thorn bushes, blown all one way by the storms, and lichened rocks that shone yellow in the sun, where the conies made deep runnels in the springing turf and the close thymes and tufted sea pinks spread.

Often on a summer evening the boat-men would glimpse the fairy tinker sitting lonesome there, with his long white whiskers blowing in the breeze.

But even as they looked he disappeared, and they would wonder had their eyes deceived them or grow uneasy, thinking he must be planning fresh rascality.

And sometimes in the winter twilight the wee glow of his horn lantern was seen near the same

One tossed the other against a boulder

place, though he never built his fire there or made it his habitation.

Nobody took much notice of his liking for the spot until one day two lumps of lads searching for a stray hen's nest happened on his secret. They had been slipping and splashing through the kelp and rock-pools, and on reaching the hillock one tossed the other against a boulder so

that it tipped with his weight, half-disclosing to
view a flat slab of iron hidden away underneath.
They lifted it very canty and found that it covered
a good-sized three-legged pot sunk in the sand,
and full to the top with fairy gold!

They knelt there, the two of them, in their little
torn breeches, with bare brown toes dusted in
between with the golden sand, and stared at the
bright guineas winking in the sunshine, all amazed
at the wonder of it. And then, before his brother
could stop him, the smaller lad reached down and
scooped up the fill of his two fists, letting the
yellow coins fall jingling through his fingers.

And with that the whole hoard vanished as if
it had never been!

For you must know that fairy gold can never
be handled by mortal man but disappears at his
first touch should he ever happen on it.

The wee lads were terribly scared by this and
were just about to take to their heels when there
was a screech behind them that woke the echoes
and set the white gulls wheeling and keening, as,
hopping and dancing, the goblin tinker lit on
them.

"Och, my gold, my gold!" he screamed, peering down into the pot and going round and round
it in a ring with the salt tears streaming from his

greedy eyes and his dirty wee hands clasping and unclasping.

He got down into the depth of the pot the better to search it, and it was terrible to hear his lamentations.

The little lads stood clinging, too frightened to move, but when the tinker's sorrow changed to anger and he started to clamber out of the pot vowing what he would do when he caught hold of them, the elder with the courage born of his fear, took and clapped on the lid, rolled the boulder over it and made for home, dragging his brother by the hand!

When they told the tale to their elders there was the queer laugh arose at the wee tinker's expense, but some of the men, out of the kindness of their hearts, set off for the hill to release him from his predicament.

And sorra a trace of him was found, then or ever!

Some said he went back to fairyland, and some that he had been seen at Killard Point and as far away as Ballykinler, but whatever happened, Tyrella sands knew him no more.

[75]

The Fairy Fiddler

THERE was a fairy fiddler
  Lived by the river Bann;
And when he played his fiddle
  The little children ran
To follow him and dance while
  The shoes fell off their feet,
And then they tripped on barefoot
  To notes both blithe and sweet.
There never was such music made
  By mortal bow or man
As that the fairy fiddler wove
  Beside the river Bann.

And when he was so minded
  He'd make the old folks hop
Hands across and round about
  Until his tune would stop.
The long years all fell away,
  Their troubles and their pain,
And if they paused for want of breath
  He'd start them off again.

There never was such magic in
　A fairy bow or man
As when the merry fiddler played
　Beside the river Bann.

While often in the gloaming
　Beneath a hawthorn tree
He'd sit and draw from heart strings
　A lilting melody;
So those who chanced to listen
　Were lovers from that day
Blessing the happy hour they heard
　The wee musician play.
Never was sweeter wooing done
　By mortal maid and man
As when the fairy fiddle sang
　Its love songs by the Bann.

SHELEG-A-BOOKIE

SHELEG-A-BOOKIE his playmates nicknamed him because they said he was slow as a snail. Sure to be touched out when they played tig, and last in the daily race from the school gate to the Withy Burn.

Jamsie laid the blame on his legs. They were not very thick, and had been apt to give out on him ever since he had the fever; but his mother said they were a right willing wee pair of legs, and only needed to be bolstered up with plenty of stirabout and lashings of sweet milk.

Down the green lanes, going roaming together, Jamsie and his mother might pause by some mossed stone or thicket of foxgloves to trace Sheleg-a-bookie, snail of the hump, creeping so

slowly with his mottled round shell clasped close
to his back and thin trail of silver stretching
behind. Jamsie's mother would say that it be-
hoved everyone to be leaving a wee trail of brightness behind, and them going through the world ;
and that it was better to be slow and sure than
quick and sorry. And small Jamsie would listen,
squeezing her hand, and resolve to eat up the
whole of his stirabout and set himself to be drink-
ing lashings of sweet milk.

There were days when his legs felt less heavy,
and he skipped and ran and made merry with his
playmates. But he was soon tired and content
to sit quietly on the ditch beside the heaped school
satchels and discarded coats—keeping count in
the games of tip-cat and taws.

And soon there was Hoppety.

Hoppety, the lame sandy-coated terrier, saved
by his pleading from a watery grave to be his close
companion and dearest possession. Hoppety of
the stub tail and sharp nose, with one droll ear
always cocked to question and three sound legs
fit to carry him gamely the length of each and
every adventure. Who had fought and tamed
Josie Quillan's big gander, that was the terror of
small girls taking the field-pad to school. Who
allowed no puss about the place but their own;

[79]

and had earned such a fame that the farmer from Tattykeeran drove with his horse and his cart, and took them away and gave them tea, when the rats in his corn-stacks and big barns were troublesome.

All the boys envied him Hoppety and would offer to trade white mice and caged jackdaws and even new clasp-knives. But something in wee Jamsie's pale twisted smile, and in the strength of his thin arms clutching Hoppety, would be answer enough for the boldest bidder, so that they must let on to have rued and not press the transaction. While Jamsie, alone with Hoppety, would explain the matter anxiously—whispering in his pricked ear that he couldn't do without him, and asking wouldn't he rather stay with one who loved him so much than be scouring the roads with the straightest and best? And Hoppety, quite frantic at such foolishness, would lick Jamsie's face and struggle to be free in order to go careering round in wide circles, barking furiously.

Once when wee Jamsie was sick and took to his bed, Hoppety stayed quietly beside him the whole of the time—nor asked to stir, even when Peter McKinstry whistled below the window and the din of a rat-hunt arose in the haggard.

There wasn't the like of Hoppety in the whole of the Nine Glens!

It was through Hoppety that they met the wee man.

There was Jamsie in the autumn woods, wading

It was through Hoppety that they met the wee man

through the red leaves and searching for conkers and ripe hazel nuts. And there was Hoppety barking at toads or chasing small birds in and out of the bramble dells. And then Hoppety was sniffing cautiously and making short runs at the moss-covered stump of a tree. While there was

[81]

the plump little man curled up asleep, with a rounded tight bundle bound fast to his back.

He was the queerest wee man you ever saw in your life, with a puckered brown face all criss-crossed with wrinkles, and a snuff-coloured suit buttoned close up to his chin. There wasn't so much as a hair on his head and he wore grey worsted stockings above pointed kid slippers. When he opened his eyes they were beady and black and stuck out like a shrimp's. And he yawned behind his hand, looking up at Jamsie, and made overtures to Hoppety—who sat down in amazement and started to thump his tail on the ground.

Jamsie didn't like to be staring too hard once the wee man had awakened, so he let on to be examining the things in his pockets and threw a conker at a fat thrush that came venturing too near.

"Well done, well done!" says the wee man approvingly in a very soft slow voice. And he clapped his small hands and made faces at the thrush so that Hoppety went chasing after it through the bracken.

"If this whole wood was cleared of birds it would be no loss," said the sleepy wee man, "and those fat greedy thrushes should be the first to go."

"You haven't a catapult about you, I suppose?" says he to Jamsie. And when Jamsie said he hadn't the wee man seemed to be disappointed.

He yawned once more and curled himself up very snugly beneath his bundle, and Jamsie, thinking he didn't want to be disturbed, prepared to slip away softly, treading on tiptoe. But with the cracking of a twig the wee man popped his eyes open and arrested Jamsie's departure with a beady stare.

Jamsie would rather have gone on about his own small concerns but he didn't know quite what to do. And just then Hoppety returned and began snuffling about the strange little gnome again, as if he couldn't make head or tail of him either.

"Shoo!" said the wee man, sobering Hoppety. "Though, indeed," says he to Jamsie, "I could have an affection for the dog—such a sportsman as he is at chasing the thrushes." And then he blinked slyly at the two of them from beneath his dropped eyelids, and seemed to debate would he say any more.

"The name that is on me," he then announced, very slowly, "is Sheleg-a-bookie; and if you think for yourself you will know without telling why

[83]

the thrushes and me can never be friends. The
little good people have me appointed as day-and-
night guardian over these woods, the way the
dodmen and moss-dwellers won't be molested;
but I get no peace of my life nor a break in the
season warding feathered marauders and ugly
green toads. There will be less need for vigilance
now and a chance to get sleeping—but when the
springtime comes round and the thrushes are
building, maybe you and the wee dog could take
a dander this way to create a disturbance and
make yourselves useful."

With that he disappeared completely in under
his pack and Jamsie lifted Hoppety and stole
away quietly.

"Child, dear!" his mother said, when the
adventure was told, " I doubt you fell asleep in
the woods and dreamed the whole of it."

But that night as Jamsie lay in the outshot bed
he heard his father and mother talking together.

It was his mother spoke first from her low stool
by the fire, bent that she might have more light
for her knitting: " Do you think, Shamus, would
there be something in the story—and maybe the
little people have taken a notion to do the child
a good turn?"

And his father's deeper voice, with its strange

SHELEG-A-BOOKIE
When he opened his eyes they were beady and black

note of tenderness: "Och, hold your whisht, woman dear, and don't fash yourself. Isn't the boy well enough and growing past his wee trouble to be our whole comfort, and a help to me about the place."

And then there was talk of a visit to some person said to be old and wise. And a drowsy blurring of all the small sounds of the houseplace, from the slow, contented ticking of the clock to the steady drip, drip of the raindrops falling off the thatch.

Came Hallowe'en with its strings of apples, and roasted nuts and dipping for pence in the churn crock. And St. Stephen's Day, when the boys paraded with a small bunch of feathers tied to a ribboned stick, all chanting loudly:

" The wren, the wren, the King of all Birds
On St. Stephen's Day he was caught in the furze!
His size is little.   His power is great.
Put your hand in your pocket and stand us a treat."

Hogmanay, when the farm hands gathered, wearing white shirts pulled over their frieze coats and tall straw hats shaped like a cone. And then the short winter days had slipped by and there was a stirring in the hedge bottoms and a noisy singing of the little runnels and grass-hidden meadow streams.

[85]   G

And when the first green buds and yellow catkins showed and the thrushes were shaping and smoothing their earth-lined nests Jamsie's mother took her small covered basket with a filling of hens' eggs and butter pats and warm soda farls. And she travelled away secretly and wouldn't say where she was going. Only on her return she set up her iron girdle in front of the fire, and made a thin flat cake of horse-corn bread which she baked very hard. And this she folded in kale leaves and gave to Jamsie to take to the woods, putting a lump of coal in his pocket as a charm against enchantment, and making him promise to do just as she bade him.

Hoppety went first, searching adventure; and now there was a shrill encounter with a hedgehog, and now a sharp scuffle as some flurried small rabbit sped towards its dark hole. While soon they were in the woods with the thrushes piping in chorus: "Goody, Goody, Goody: Bo-peep, Bo-peep, Bo-peep: How d'ye do? How d'ye do?"

Jamsie went straight to the tree-stump where he had seen the wee man and let down the kale leaves and cake of corn-bread. Then he turned the lump of coal in his pocket and chanted out loud, as his mother had taught him:

[86]

" Sheleg-a-bookie
Come from the green dell,
For here one is waiting
A small wish to tell."

But, though he stayed still for a long while,
no wee man appeared, and there were only the
whispering echoes of the woods and calling of
birds from the hazel bushes.

Then he minded the little man's stern war on
the thrushes and set out with Hoppety to patrol
the slippery green paths of the glen—where last
year's dark leaves piled dank underfoot and the
long moist roots of the beech trees twisted and
spread. Here and there the slow snails went
creeping in the patches of sunlight; and when
you lifted a stone Meg-wi-mony-legs lay drowsing,
or the busy moss-dwellers hurried out on small
errands. Clocks and slaters, and wee willie-
weavers, and spotted bright ladybirds.

It was dinner-time before they got back to the
tree-stump—to find that the cake of corn-bread
and the kale leaves had vanished! So that
Jamsie went speeding away home, all excitement,
eager to find and get telling his mother.

But she warned him not to be saying a word
to anyone and promised to let him go back very
soon with another wee offering for Sheleg-a-bookie.

[87]

Many a ramble did Jamsie take through the
woods with Hoppety; and he came to have an
interest in the tiny people of the
underworld of leaves and roots and
mosses. But never a glimpse did
he get of Sheleg-a-bookie.

One month passed,
and two, and three; and

The cake of corn-bread and the kale leaves had vanished!

then it was midsummer with the trees in full
leaf and a green crowding of branches. And on
a showery June morning Jamsie went down

through the glen and spread his small feast on
the mossed table of the tree stump, before sounding his call:

"Sheleg-a-bookie,
Come from the green dell."

He wandered away then, threading the ferned
footpaths and dead forests of the bluebell stems;
and on his return to the log behold, there was the
little round man complacently finishing his repast,
with the front of his surcoat all dusted with corn-
meal!

"You're the best of a boy," says he to wee
Jamsie, "and you have only to name your wish
for it to be granted this minute. What is it that
you are after requiring for yourself?"

"I could wish," said Jamsie, timorous now that
things had got so far, "for a better pair of legs,
that would be speedier and stronger, and fit to
carry me any length without tiring."

"The whole trouble with deluded mortal men,"
said the wee hob severely, "is the way they must
be speeding about their concerns. From now on
you'll spend your time wearing out boots, and
I'm heart scalded to be furthering a notion that's
tee-totally against my own way of thinking. I'll
be neither next nor near these parts again, but
when you recall Sheleg-a-bookie always mind

[89]

this: The morrow's still another day—and maybe the slower you travel the more you'll be seeing."

With that he gave a fat sort of chuckle to himself and disappeared so suddenly in under the tree root that Jamsie might have doubted had he been there at all, except for the remaining crumbs of corn-bread and pale ribs of the kale leaves left lying on the moss.

From that day on he never sighted the strange little man, while his own wish was granted and he grew to possess the strongest and longest pair of legs in the Nine Glens of Antrim. But no matter how fast they took him he'd always spare time to be doing a good turn, or to study the small unnoticed wonders of the world; and out on their rambles he had only to say " Sheleg-a-bookie " to send Hoppety sniffing about among the roots and the mosses.

THE FAIRIES of the LONE BOG ROADS

YEARS ago in the lone bog-lands of Connaught there used to be hundreds of fairies.

They were strange desolate wee people, dark-skinned and no taller than a turf sod; all hoary-headed the way you might be mistaking them for the white bog blossoms, and often those returning from their caelie in the still moonlight heard the thin song of them rising on the wind.

Some said it was only the breezes stirring in the tall marsh grasses, or the screech of an owl or far cry of the plover, but there were others who knew it was the wandering fairies, and them lost and calling on the lone bog roads.

Oft-times in March weather, when the storm-thrush whistled and the thorn bushes showed their first green buds, a kind of madness came over them and those with eyes to see glimpsed them tumbling and playing themselves on the

Riding the brown hares in and out amongst the rocks

golden mosses; giving each other a back and riding the brown hares in and out amongst the rocks and through the gaps in the whin bushes.

And the turf-cutters, busy wielding their slender shining blades with the raised sharp edge, would see the patient ass that stood with his waiting creels throw up his head and start a canter, sporting himself, with the wee folk chasing at his heels.

The lassies that wrought with the men, spreading the dark wet sods for sun and wind to dry, would leave a piece of horse-corn bread, or a lashing of butter-milk, and them going home in the evening-time, the way their work would be made easier for them on the morrow, or maybe the clamping done for them overnight.

For the fairies never forgot a kindness; and it was telling anyone who got the right side of them or made them indebted.

By one big stretch of bogland, where the cutting had long ceased to be, and nothing grew but the springing heather and close myrtles and bilberry bushes, there lived a poor old crippled man.

Red Hughie of the Rawe was the name people put on him, though his hair that had been bright was dusted now with the frosts of years.

He was bent almost double with the rheumatic pains and could only manage to pull himself along with the help of two sticks; and he lived alone in a wee cabin built into the bare hillside.

It was a queer, cramped dwelling-place, thatched over with dried whins and heather, and the lads who hunted the wild fowl's eggs, or searched for berries on the steep slopes above,

[93]

would often find themselves on its roof unbeknownst, not being able to tell it from the surrounding wastes until they would see the thread
of blue smoke rising from the chimney.

There was a small enclosure walled in with
stones that Red Hughie in the days of his health
and strength had reclaimed from the marshland.
Just a wee patch for his potatoes, and a field for
his oats and sparse hay crop, but these had long
since fallen fallow, and the moor was fast taking
them to itself again.

He was far away from the help of friend or
neighbour and sometimes it would be questioned
was he dead or alive, unless he had been seen laying in his little store of provisions, or that people
happened to glimpse the glow of his rushlight
shining through the darkness like a tethered star.

A river ran beyond his wee domain that rose
in the mountains and had waters stained brown
with the peat streams filtering into it on its way.
It was bridged here and there with flat boulders,
or stepping-stones, the way the herdsmen and
farm-dwellers could cross when tending the cattle
that sought the sweet short feeding of the lowlands; and it was by the crossing near his small
abode that old Hughie came on a fairy one wild
day in a sad predicament.

You must know that the bog-fairies had to travel on their own two feet after the manner of mortal men and didn't this wee fellow, attempting to leap from slab to slab across the river swollen with autumn rains, find himself stranded in the middle.

He stood on a big boulder, awash with the flood waters

He stood on a big boulder, awash with the flood waters, afraid either to go backwards or to jump the chasm that yawned before him; and Hughie shouted to him to hold on and he would be with him, though, indeed, he had his own work set in order to reach the slab without slipping into the stream which ran fast and deep.

[95]

But, with great exertion, he managed to get near enough to reach out his crutch and steady the fairy man from stone to stone.

Old Hughie was about to reprimand him for being so foolhardy and endangering both their lives, but before he could come at himself to choose his words the wee hob disappeared without so much as a word of thanks.

"And bad scran to you for lack of manners!" said the decent man, pulling the quelching shoes off himself and seeking the scanty comfort of his own hearth-stone.

He thought no more about the affair until he rose the next morning, and found the fire that he had raked overnight burning bright, and a heap of gathered turf and dry bog-wood left convenient in the chimney corner.

A pail of spring water stood ready for the filling of his kettle, and some handy person had been at work sweeping and dusting the house, the way he didn't know himself when he looked around.

All through the winter days the wee people fetched and carried for him; and at planting time his corn was sown in secret, so that the green blades came piercing through where idle grass-grown furrows had been before, and his potato patch had its neatly set ridges.

And often he would find a speckled trout left lying on a handful of wet rushes, adorning his empty platter, or a present of plovers' eggs, and them warm from the nest.

He didn't dare to boast to his neighbours of the luck he was in, and those that passed thought he must have gained a new strength, and yet were surprised to see that he still dragged himself as painfully as ever on his sticks.

Once or twice at the sight of the glowing sods they might have a wee suspicion, but nobody grudged him what firing he could gather, and no roadside turf stack was found depleted.

And then a grasping farmer, whose cutting ran adjacent, cast covetous eyes on the well-cared small holding, lying snug and green in the shelter of the hillside, and sought to evict old Hughie, claiming past rights of possession.

Hughie was greatly put about, seeing his wee independence taken from him, and himself cut adrift from his only home.

He was standing disconsolate at his house door one evening, brooding over his new trouble, when the farmer hove in sight, looking very purposeful.

Old Hughie saw him start to cross the river and knocked out his clay pipe on the door-post, finding the comfort gone from it, but no visitor appeared

[97]

and after a while he heard a shouting and muttering coming from the direction of the stepping-stones.

He dragged himself down to the river, as quickly as he was able, and there was his enemy stuck in mid-stream, powerless to move hand or foot the way the bog-fairies had him fixed!

He besought old Hughie's aid, but though Hughie did his best, and pulled and tugged away, he couldn't effect a rescue, and there the farmer had to stay until the stars came twinkling out to mirror themselves in the dark water and a pale moon rose and slowly waned.

With the sound of the first lark's song the farmer recovered the use of his limbs, and made the best of his way home in a very poor case. He never was seen in the locality again; and his children's children told of the spell that the angry bog-fairies put on him.

Old Hughie is dead long ago; but the remains of his dwelling may still be seen, and where it stood is said to be fairies' ground to this day.

WAG-
AT-
THE-
WALL

THERE was once a wee Clonakilty woman with
the busiest tongue in the whole county of Cork.
It moved always, like a leaf in the wind, and not
a thing could pass her door but she must know
the ins and outs of it or lose her night's sleep.

She was a wee, sharp, spinster-body, and none
grudged her an interest in the love stories and
talk of the country-side, excepting when she took
to romancing on her own account or made up
news for the want of it—a thing that often happened, events being slow in her locality.

She lived alone in a small neat house by the

roadside with a flower garden in front and a low white wall against which she was mostly to be found leaning, clacking and watching and discussing her neighbours, so that people called her "Wag-at-the-Wall."

She knew rightly the name that was on her and it made her angry, but only gave her that much more to be talking about and her tongue went speeding ever, prodigal as running water!

Half her fault arose from loneliness, for she was kind-hearted and would run a mile to do a good turn. There wasn't a better nurse, or a cleverer hand with churn and poultry, and she kept her house like a new pin, so tidy that virtue became a discomfort, for you were nearly afraid to sit down in it! But folk were loath to avail themselves of her willing services since she couldn't be trusted to keep a thing to herself and since nobody wants innocent concerns carried beyond their own door-step.

Well it happened that she was returning from a May fair with the covered basket that had held her eggs packed with her week's provisions and a new flower to sew in her last year's bonnet, stepping out briskly as she neared home and thought of the fire to be lighted and kettle boiled before she could take her ease.

WAG-AT-THE-WALL

He only grunted and blew out great clouds of tobacco smoke

It was getting dusk; but at the cross-roads within sight of her own turning, she came on a small man crouched in the ditch with the bowl of his long clay pipe glowing redly in the shadows.

She passed the time of day, and, knowing him for a stranger to the neighbourhood, stopped to probe where he was from and to try and find out his name and business.

Very poor satisfaction she got, for he only grunted and blew out great clouds of his tobacco smoke—seeming to be hard of hearing or un-mannerly. So she made to leave him and had gone a few steps when he called after her: "Wag-at-the-Wall!"

She was back at his side in two hops, giving him all sorts of scolding and abuse and thanking him not to mis-name her or to be passing remarks where they were unasked, but she made a poor hand of him for he just twinkled and smoked. And when she paused for breath, practised as she was, he repeated his offence and chuckled at his own sly joke and her bad temper.

She left him again at that and swished off down the road, her indignation stiff upon her, and on opening her door and lighting her candle who should she see sitting by her cold hearth but the same wee rogue—waiting to continue the argument!

She thought he must have slipped past her unbeknownst and was so taken aback that words failed her for the space of a minute, and then he was ordered to leave the house on the instant, under threat of sharp pains and penalties. Though there he sat in derision and not one foot did he put before the other! She took her besom to him but made no impression and then she became afeared, knowing him for some imp of darkness, and started to plead, begging him to begone and offering him money to help him on his way. But, deaf alike to beseeching and abuse, the intruder smoked and sat, watching her with his twinkling bright eyes and saying over to himself, as if meditating and amused: "Wag-at-the-Wall! Wag-at-the-Wall!"

There he remained for the whole of three long days; and the poor wee woman was in a pitiful plight, dreading that he would be discovered by her neighbours and unable to eat or sleep for scolding and fretting.

All her vexation and bewailing passed unheeded and it seemed that she was never to be rid of him: but when she grew quiet and resigned to her penance he disappeared; and over by where he had sat was a fine large wag-at-the-wall clock, ticking away its best!

She tried to pull it down, and would have burned it then and there, but she couldn't move it from the hook, so it remained to stare her in

Deaf alike to beseeching and abuse the intruder smoked and sat

the face and to be commented on by her friends —when they had time to spare from wondering about her own silence and discretion!

For she had learned her lesson and had such a fear of the goblin's return that she scarcely dared to leave her hearth-stone in case she should

[103]

find him sitting by it when she got back. While the new clock ticked so loudly and continuously that you couldn't hear yourself speaking above the sound of it!

In the years it came to be the only reminder of her old nickname, for she lived to be respected as a decent, quiet, wee woman and ever-ready friend to the whole countryside in time of trouble.

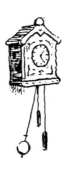

Bog Blossoms

THE deep pools hold the shadow of flying cloud,
Dark gathered peat, and tangled gold of gorse;
Green rushes, tawny-tasselled, and bent thorns
Lit by the leaping flame of ripened haws.

Moist winds blown inland from the distant sea,
Sweet with the scent of heather and wild thyme,
And sun-warmed bracken, linger on the plain
Where the bog blossoms spread their silken rime;

Like flowers some cunning water-sprite bewitched,
Leaving all hoary-headed to fulfil
Their length of days; knowing a lost loveliness
When stars are strung and moonbeams drench the hill.

THE FAIRY OF THE MILL STREAM

By the wooded shores of Lough Erne, at that part where the lower lake narrows into a placid stream before gathering strength for its swifter passage to the sea, there once dwelt a miller and his three daughters.

One had a dark pride, and one a sleek fairness, but the youngest, Rose Ann, had the brown lure of lake waters, and her heart was like ripened corn.

The miller had lost the wife of his youth, and for that his father's love had been the kindlier, but his youngest-born knew her mother's tenderness and came to be as the light of his eyes. From the time she could walk she followed him closely wheresoever he went, sitting contentedly on the heaped sacks of wheat and barley as he busied himself about the mill, and at night bringing her creepie-stool against his knee while he rested from his labours. So that soon he was fretful if she strayed beyond his call, and would have no hand but hers to minister to his needs.

Suitors came in plenty; and the elder girls married early and went from home, taking fine dowries to their husbands; but Rose Ann, his "heart o' corn," lived on with her father in the old millhouse where always you heard the slow splashing of the great water-wheel and the sound of the river as it ran.

Quietly the years of her girlhood passed over her. Springtimes when wallflower and daffodil scented her garden plot and the twittering swallows returned to the thatch. Sunny hours, and green summer pathways set deep in bearded grass and foaming meadowsweet, with the brown bees noisy in the clover bloom. Lulled autumn days of yellow corn stooks and drifting leaves; and winters when spangled hazel wands wove a still enchantment, witching the frozen pools, and creaking farm wagons drew piled dusty loads of winnowed grain.

It was in a mid-May gloaming that she went

wandering down by the river bank, plucking the varnished kingcups where they grew, and there came on a little old man fishing away his best.

He wore a cutaway coat, knee-breeches, and

He saluted Rose Ann like an elfin grandee

buckled shoes, with a three-cornered hat the colour and texture of bulrushes, and he saluted Rose Ann like an elfin grandee—motioning her to step softly the way she wouldn't disturb the trout nibbling at his bait.

[108]

She stayed shyly to wish him good luck at his sport—standing with the bright flowers spilling from her apron, so fair a distraction that the wee angler discarded his line the better to be tempting her smiles.

He opened his neat basket of peeled sally-rods to show her his catch—three very small fish of the kind named miller's-thumb laid out in state on a handful of sedge grass, and you would have thought each one a pike he was so boastful and made so much of the landing of them. But Rose Ann humoured him pleasantly in his wee conceit and then must sit down beside him on the bank while he demonstrated his skill and told of past achievements.

Gently the river went flowing between its green banks and flowering rushes, the mayflies glancing above the burnished shallows where the steeped buds of thorn and elder eddied and sailed, with now a blown orchard petal or floating white feather from the duck-pond round the bend. The stillness of late day folded the meadows, broken only by the faint bleating of pent lambs or cuckoo's call from a leafy dingle, and the small voice of the grasshopper was loud in the silence that the bees had left.

She lingered out a golden hour until the vanished sun bade her hasten home to prepare the evening meal. But before the miller came she filled a tankard with their best home-brew and buttered a piece of barley bread to take to the angler by the mill-race, and he rose to bow farewell and tender stately thanks—leaving the tankard where she would be sure to find it when he went away.

Afterwards she often watched but never saw him again; and then all else was forgotten in the sore grief and trouble that beset her. For her father slipped whilst loading grain and was gravely injured—lying in a high fever and at death's door for long days and rising at length, changed and enfeebled, nevermore to be the same strong able man.

The work of the mill went on, but missed his guiding hand, and gradually the custom of the countryside passed to another, and the place began to have a sadly forlorn and neglected appearance. Silt clogged and choked the mill-race, and tall plantains and nettles sprang up unchecked, hiding the river bank and silent mossy wheel. While water voles, grown bold, devoured the scattered grain, and bats clustered undisturbed where thick powdery cobwebs draped the whitened beams.

The sisters came with their husbands offering advice but giving little help. And sometimes the miller sought to rouse himself and exert his failing powers; but more often sat brooding and ailing in the chimney corner, wholly dependent on his daughter's love, yet scarcely conscious of her care.

So fast misfortunes crowded upon them with each succeeding year that the old happiness and tranquillity seemed as a dream in the ever-present reality of their distress, and soon their little store of money dwindled and was gone.

They were saved from greater affliction by the kindly remembrance of many a poor neighbour, to whom Rose Ann had once given of her abundance and who now sought to aid and comfort her in adversity. And she tended her hives and poultry and sat diligently at her spinning, always striving to cheer and console the one so dear to her, and making no complaint or plea of misfortune. But her eyes grew shadowed and her brown braids streaked with early silver; whilst the fear of losing the mill and seeing her father homeless and broken in his old age was ever with her, and caused her to lie weeping in the lonesome watches of the night.

It chanced on a day when her trouble seemed sorest and her need most pressing that she made ready to scour out the houseplace—thinking to busy her hands and ease the sad burden of her thoughts.

Taking her wooden bucket, she went away to the mill-stream and kneeling down by the river bank dipped it deep down amid the shifting sedge grass and floating flat lily leaves. But when she would have drawn it back she found it entangled and sucked out beyond her reach—so that she rose to seek a crooked stick or forked bough with which to clutch at the handle.

And gazing about her it seemed that she glimpsed an attentive short figure outlined against the cleft trunk of a pollard-ash . . . Swallow-tailed coat, corded knee breeches, and square-buckled shoes; with a three-cornered hat that had the soft sheen and texture of plush-tipped bulrushes.

Yet when she ran forward there was only the flecked sunshine falling through the branches and the long shadows stretching to the water's edge.

Intent on retrieving her pail, she pulled at a withy wand; and it was then that she dislodged the plastered loam seaming the cleft in the ash —disclosing to view a leather purse hidden in the hollowed trunk and half buried in dry leaf-mould. The bag broke and crumbled at her touch, while in amongst the twigs a shower of tarnished gold-pieces lay scattered—enough to weight down her apron and sound a chiming song of hope and comfort as she made her way home . . . a prayer of thankfulness on her lips, and a tender thought spared for her wee fairy friend and companion of a sunny hour!

Prosperity returned; and an honest young miller came to work for them and send the great mill-wheel turning merrily once more. He loved his master's daughter at first sight and they married and lived happily. But better than the fairy dowry she brought to him was the golden worth and treasure of her own true heart.

BOIRCHE of the BENS

In the days when every fair green had roped tournament place around which sporting squireen and tattered gossoon might gather to cheer the giants of the ring, there stood near the town of Dungannon, on the Donaghmore road, the forge of Shane Rafftery, wheelwright and smith, known to the whole countryside.

A great fighter and wrestler, and for long champion of three counties, he was said to have challenged all comers in Ulster and those beyond the borders. Men would tramp miles that he might shoe their horses or mend a broken plough-share just to get looking at him or be hearing of his exploits in the prize-ring; and tales of his valour were carried and sung like the legends of olden-time heroes.

One May morning Shane Rafftery leaned

against his anvil watching the world as it passed the smithy, when presently a shifty-looking tinker-man hove in sight straddling a grey mare. Her ribs showed and her head was drooping, and she limped painfully on small, badly-shod feet; but for all her dejection there lingered a trace of gallantry and fine breeding that brought Shane Rafftery striding out to accost the Romany.

"Hold on a minute, Gipsy," he called. "And what might you be doing with the little horse?"

The tinkerman, flattered by his notice, pulled up to tell how he had got her at the Moy horse fair in exchange for his own donkey and a make-weight of mountain-dew, on account of her being lame and unfitted for farm work; and the smith, with a rising anger on him, looked at the way the mare was galled and wealed, and at the hard eyes and stout ash plant of the sinewy gipsy man.

"Am I known to you?" asked Shane Rafftery of the tinkerman, advancing a step, and the fellow, suddenly wary, nodded his head and pulling at the rope reins hit the mare a whang with his stick.

"Sell me the little horse," Shane Rafftery said. "I'll make it worth your while, but if you won't trade I'll fight you for her, and then go to break the head of the callous rogue who sold her away to be dragging out her heart."

[115]

" 'Twill be a great inconvenience to myself," whined the tinkerman, " and me looking to her to be pulling the little cart along the roads, and missing the use of my strong able donkey; but I'd be willing to oblige you, Shane Rafftery, because of your grand fighting fame, and the reputation that is on you up and down the country for honesty and fair dealing."

" I'll not cheat you," said the smith grimly, and counted money from his belt into the tinker's dirty hand. " That's all you'll get, and I'm deriding myself for a fool of the world that I'd stoop to have truck with you. The mare will likely enough fall dead on me within the week, but she'll die easy and I'll have a better taste in my mouth when we're both well rid of you."

Shoving the halter into Shane Rafftery's big fist, the tinkerman turned in his tracks and went hurrying back to the town to boast of his cunning and wet the transaction; and the smith led the little mare into the forge.

" Come up, girl," he ordered, running his hand over her with a gentleness, " and let me decide what the ruling is. There are those who'd declare that you had been fairy-ridden, but nothing ails you that isn't accountable to bad usage and starvation. 'Tis a delicate head and fine neck you have on you, and slender enough wee trotters if they were fit to carry you the way they should."

He raised a hoof into his leather apron to strip off the clumsy ill-made shoe, and the mare lipped his shirt-sleeve and seemed to speak to him with her soft dark eyes.

"Would you be telling me," said Shane Raff-tery, "that I ought to turn you out into the wee paddock beyont once I have the shoes stripped from you? Well, indeed now, the same notion occurred to myself. For the next six months you shall be a lady of leisure, and instead of grazing your shins by the roadside there'll be the sweet grasses to lip and a bran mash or wheen of oats just to vary the sameness. 'Tis myself is the terrible bruiser with a reputation on me to be giving and taking hard knocks; but cruelty to the helpless falls short of my creed, and if my heart wasn't as sore for you I'd be crazed with anger!"

For six months and more the little grey mare took her ease in the paddock, swishing her tail at the gadflies and moving from tuft to tuft of the sweet pasture grasses. Her ribs covered and her feet healed, and she became the petted fondling of the smith's wife and children. Sometimes she

[117]   I

would be docile enough for the younger ones to
ride round and round on her back, and on other
days she took skittish fancies so that they couldn't
approach her. But a whistle from Shane Rafftery
always brought her cantering to gate or fence ;
and when she was fit to carry him they travelled
everywhere together as he went to one county
or another in defence of his title, so that in
time the little grey mare became as famous as
Shane Rafftery's self.

He took to saying that she brought him luck,
and when he emerged victorious from his con-
quests it was to the little grey mare that he
ascribed the credit. " If you ever lost her," his
wife foretold, " you'd be roaming the country
searching for the track of her shoe; and fit to
challenge the giant Finn McCool and all the
powers of the leprechauns to be getting her
back!"

Strangely foreboding the same words turned
out to be, for three years to the day that he first
set eyes on her the grey mare disappeared, and
neither trace nor tidings could the smith discover
though he sought far and wide, and had every
horse dealer in the province out helping him on
the job. Not a gipsy encampment escaped a
visit, and he'd stand hawk-eyed on every fair

ground; but it seemed that the little horse had
been elfshot and spirited away.

He had almost given up hope of any news when
a red-headed mountainy gossoon arrived at the
forge.   A tattered coat was on him and he walked
barefoot, but his eyes
were honest.

"Would this shoe be-
long to your little horse?"
said he.

A red-headed mountainy gossoon arrived at the forge

Shane Rafftery took a quick look at the
shoe and a longer look at the tattered gossoon.
"That's my grey mare's shoe," he replied, "and
I'm waiting for you to tell me just where you came
on it."

"My name's MacMahon," said the red-haired boy, "and I'm tramping from Tollymore in the Kingdom of Mourne, to get finding yourself. I once saw you beat the Annalong Wonder, and when I heard about the loss of your little horse I had a wish to get serving you. The shoe I found by the Sliddery Ford, but maybe you'll not believe in my story when I tell you the whole of it."

"I am trusting you," said Shane Rafftery the smith. "Tell on."

"I was fishing the Shimna River," the mountainy lad told him, "and me herding my cattle among the peaks with a winding mist on the highlands and the cry of the curlews sounding strangely as though they'd be laying a spell. When I reached the top of a pass, where the stone circle is, the mist cleared, and I heard a thin bleating and saw a herding of small animals all jostling one another and huddled and not contented at all. There were wee creachy lambs and calves crying and a shepherd's dog lonesome without his master; while at the edge of the gathering a grey mare moved restlessly, with ears pricked for a whistle and a whinny out of her now and then, and her pawing the shelving rocks. A wonder grew on me as I watched, and I was a

[120]

mind to be leading off the grey mare, on the chance that she'd be the one I'd heard tell of as belonging to yourself; but before I'd rightly decided the matter there came a fluting music on the wind, and a great hairy man came from be-tween the crags. He had a tow head and large ears and shepherd's garb on him; but when I

Me knowing him for Boirche of the Bens

saw his goat's feet a trembling took me, and me knowing him for Boirche of the Bens, who can draw the will out of you with his playing. I jouked down out of sight, afraid for my life, and

[121]

when I got courage to glance again wasn't his shadowy shape fading among the rocks, and him leading the little grey mare by the halter with the creachy lambs and the rest trooping after to the note of his pipe."

"Take me to where you saw this happening," said Shane Rafftery, the smith, "and I will put gold in your hand, and be your friend for life."

"Good enough," said the mountainy lad, "but all I'd ask would be for you to apprentice me to your trade, and show me the clinch that caught out the Annalong Wonder."

Travelling fast and far, Shane Rafftery and his tatter-coated guide came at length to the Mourne country and the crooked passes among the majestic peaks. Great Donard flew white banners of cloud, and everywhere was a glory of heather in bloom; and the tumbling hill streams sang a song of high summer that was fit to drown the magical music of Boirche of the Bens.

Through the Hare's Gap and across the Spelga Pass to the Deer's Meadow with the towering heights of Commedagh and Bearnagh and Bingian, and Meelbeg and Meelmore piercing the skyline like jagged teeth. The mountainy lad,

hardy and sure-footed, led the way, and after him
strode Shane Rafftery with his broad shoulders
braced and his searching eyes, but neither the
granite dust of the quarries nor the dried mud
of the quagmires revealed track or trace of the
grey mare's small shoe.

On the ninth day of their search they reached
the Plain of the Rath and started the steep ascent
of Slieve Donard's self. The sun was hot on them
as they climbed, and the air drowsy with the
humming of bees and scent of the heather and
red thyme; and when they neared the pool of
the Saint that lies cupped against the mountain's
crown, Boirche of the Bens lay stretched flat and
sleeping on a bed of bracken, his breath coming
in gusts and his magical pipes loosed from his
grasp. Within a Shield-ring of stones a herd of
small domestic animals and flock of birds grazed
or stood quietly, and roaming apart from the rest
the grey mare pricked ears and came cantering
swiftly at their approach.

Sleeking her neck and whispering wee endear-
ments, Shane Rafftery bade the lad take charge
of her, while he, himself, crept stealthily to where
Boirche lay sprawled and stooping laid bold quick
hands on the magic pipes. The tow-headed goat-
man stirred but did not wake, and beckoning

silently the smith urged on the lad with the mare and waded them out into the shallows of Donard's blest pool.

"Ochance a nee oh!" shivered the mountainy lad, "what has you at this trickery at all? Sure when the goat-man wakes and misses his pipes he'll be neither to hold nor to bind, and matched against such a magic-worker we're as good as lost men this minute."

"Never fear," said Shane Rafftery, and let a sudden roar out of him that startled the echoes and sent the brown conies hopping towards their dark holes.

Lazily the goat-man roused himself and reached out a hand for his pipes, and when he was reared to his full height he showed as slim and strangely shapely, with quick, light movements as he trod over the heather to where the blue lake sparkled among the rocks. Standing on the shore he gazed across the rippling shallows at Shane Rafftery, his long hands, lacking the feel of the pipes, hanging empty and powerless-looking—but in his eyes was a queer, yellow light and a brooding magic.

A sudden weakness like a swooning came on Shane Rafftery; but he waded out still farther and called loudly above the quiet lap-lap of the

[124]

water—purposefully and yet conscious of his mortal frailty.

"Harken," commanded the smith, "for I have things I must be saying to you, Boirche of the Bens. Harm may not befall those who stand ringed by the blest waters of Donard; and I call on the Saint's self to be our go-between. Will you give in that we should reason together?"

"Say on, Shane Rafftery," said Boirche of the Bens.

"I am not seeking to avenge your black arts or to probe the cruel mischief of your heart," said the smith. "Through cunning you stole my little horse, and by the same token I have your pipes. Grant us leave to go from here without let or hindrance, and give your word that you'll take no spite at us in future, and I'll hand back what I stole. But if we can't agree I'll hurl the pipes into the middle of the lake where no power of yours will be fit to redeem them; and if you'll meet me man for man, with only the strength of our sinews to be tested, I challenge you in mortal combat for my little mare, and abide by the outcome of the struggle."

The goat-man laughed on a sudden, and his eyes were teasing and merry as the eyes of a

[125]

small boy caught out in a rascality, who hopes by cajolery to escape his deserts.

"Och, Shane Rafftery," said he, "am I worse than the mischievous elves who seize the playthings from children for no better reason than that their hearts were too set on them? Lead away the grey mare and the whole gathering of fondling things that I took on me to decoy: the creachy lambs from the farmer's children, and the slit-tongued raven that belongs to the stonecutter, and there's a one-eyed goose should be restored to an old spinning cummer, and the shepherd's dog is thinking long for his master. Give me back my pipes, Shane Rafftery, and more power to your elbow; and may you hear my music in your heart when your strength gives out on you, and you toothless and hugging the chimney corner and thinking back to past victories and the days of your youth."

Late in the evening Shane and the boy reached the foot of the mountain and started on the long road that would be leading them home. They took it in turns to ride the grey mare, and after them trooped the fondling creatures that had regained their liberty. The shepherd received his old dog with joy; and a white-haired spin-

ning cummer gave them a blessing in exchange
for her gander; whilst the raven flew to the
stone-cutter's shoulder and croaked "Howdy?
Howdy? Howdy?" ten times running.

People hurried to their doors to see Shane
Rafftery ride by with his spoils of victory, and
every boreen disclosed a claimant for a freshly-
weaned fondling calf
or creachy lamb. When
he reached Tyrone of the
Bushes there remained

The raven flew to the stonecutter's shoulder

with him only his little grey mare, and a tatter-
coat boy who trod pridefully in his wake, as
though he squired a warrior and carried his
shining shield.

[127]

The Magic Lake

THERE is a secret pool, dew-fed and still,
Ringed by the blossomed gorse and
    heather hill,
Whose waters, changing not with drought
    or cold,
Know sailing pomp of cloud and mirrored
    gold;
Shy creatures of the glen stoop there to
    drink
And sleeping lilies freight the shallow
    brink.

Never fish swims, dark roach or speckled trout,
Darting from burnished stones swift in and out;
Sunken deep down, yet strangely green and near,
The swinging elfland city may appear,
With trancéd turret reared and lights to stream
As now the sunset colours glance and gleam.

Red mosses bind the edge, and dim blue flowers
So small that they might gem Titania's bowers;
The heron drowses; and the dragon-fly
Makes minute music there, sustained and high;
And when moon-dappled shadows stretch and bar
The tangled reeds net each a silver star.

A Sowing of Heartsease

THERE was once a wee gnome with a great taste for horticulture and sorra a square foot of soil to be calling his own.

He must content himself with tending the cottage gardens and nursery plots in his locality, and many's the gay flower border and neat onion bed owed its fame to his secret ministrations. But sure it was poor work stealing to weed and hoe by moonlight or at early dawn when the dews and hoar-frosts lay white on the cabbages. After a while he began to hanker for a wee domain of his own, where he might have liberty to be working at his tasks without a fear of somebody catching him by the leg should he chance to be taken by surprise. He saw that he must absent himself from the haunts of men so he hied away to a lone island, and on a snug plateau sheltered beneath tall cliffs and fanned by sea breezes commenced his labours.

He dug and delved and cleared stones till the sweat poured from him like water through a cullender and the wee hands of him were calloused and blistered as elm-tree boles. The wilderness of whins gave him the most trouble, for as fast as he cleared and uprooted they rose again lusty and wayward. But soon he had them trimmed and subdued until they lay short, and close as a shining carpet, and in their shade he set the flowering heaths in endless variety.

It was as pretty a pleasance as you would see the world over, with the colour of it fit to dazzle your eyes and you coming on it in the height of mid-summer. Such a glory of gold was in it and patchings of reds and purples as if the sunset hues lay tangled in the rocks. He had beds of blue scabious and yellow hawksbeard, with drifts of horned poppy and cushions of sea-pinks. There were speedwells and saltworts and close creeping thymes; while in between grew snapdragons and toadflax and wee elfin blossoms he gathered and transplanted from the dear knows where. Should there be a fissure or lichened crevice, there he set ladyfern and saxifrage and silver silene. And he edged his rock pools with harebells and delicate mosses, and had a stretch of greensward where the elves and fays of his acquaintance might be sporting and playing themselves at the full of the moon.

No mortal foot wandered to his retreat, for the few people on the island were mainly concerned with their farming and fishing and had little time to be exploring the creeks and hidden shore places. Now and then he might hear a faint call from some boatman or a child's laughter borne on the breeze, but mostly there was no sound save the whining of the gulls and sough of the restless waves that beat and thundered at the foot of the cliffs. Until one day when he returned from an expedition, with his pockets stuffed with roots and his breeches all loam, whom should he come on but a slim lassie standing disconsolate within the charmed circle of his rocks—and her roaring and crying with her face hidden in her hands.

The wee gnome dropped a cluster of gentian and two harts-tongue ferns and stood staring in the greatest dismay; for women he could never abide—and young women were the worst of all, skipping and teasing and plucking choice buds to be adorning themselves.

He pulled at his beard and dusted his jerkin and removed the round hat from his head, only

to look at it and put it on again. And then he
rattled his pick and shovel and shuffled his feet,
so that the lassie peeped between her fingers, and
let out a wee screech when
she saw him glowering
at her.

"What ails you?" says
he, very gruff. " And is

Whom should he come upon but a slim lassie

there no place else on the whole island you must
be snooking in only this?"

He let on to be ill-mannered, hoping to chase
her and discourage reappearances, but she only
sobbed the louder, with her dark curls falling

[132]

BOIRCHE OF THE BENS
" Sell me the little horse," Shane Rafftery said

about her face and the blue eyes of her drowned in tears.

"Sure I came here for heart's ease," sighed she, "and aren't you the hardened wee man that would deny a poor girl the comfort of solitude —and her doing you no harm, nor asking to detain you."

"Heartsease," says the wee gnome, pricking up his ears, "'deed I heard tell of that, true enough, but I haven't it, to my knowledge, in the whole of my collection. Could you describe it to me now—and have you any idea what genus it is and if it grows from cuttings or seeds?"

He warmed to her in spite of himself, since she appeared to have some wit, but with the next breath she dispelled the illusion.

"Och, amn't I the unhappy girl," she moaned, "with no one to befriend me, and my stepmother beating and scolding me, day in day out, and contriving to marry me away from my lover. I swore to him that I would be true and await his return from the long voyage he is on, but I am sorely ill-used and beset and my poor heart like to break with the trouble that's in it. If you could help me to heart's ease, little man, it would be a wonder of heaven!"

"Well, indeed now, I might," said he, overcome

[133]   K

by this tale of her woes and determining to aid
her. "Sure I heard of it often—but whether it
be leaves to brew or roots to powder I couldn't
be saying. Let you take courage from this out;
for if heartsease is to be found I'm your boyo.
And if it isn't on the island we'll search some place
else," says he.

She looked at him wonderingly, smiling through
her tears to see him so earnest, and many's the
time after she went out of her way to visit the
gnome's garden and talk to the kindly wee man
of her troubles.

In truth she soon had him so charmed that he
would have gone to the world's end to further her
desires; and there wasn't an inch of the island
he didn't search diligently in his quest for heartsease.

At last he made up his mind that it couldn't
be there; and when he got a boat rowing over to
the mainland he hid himself away among the
kegs and heaped sheepskins and was landed in
the long run at Portballintrae.

He was hardly off the quayside when he walked
into a Fellow of Trinity.

"My service to your reverence," says he, doffing
his hat, "and could you tell me the nature and
meaning of heartsease?"

[134]

" Is it ' *viola tricolor* ' or ' *Hollonia palustris* ' ? "
says the Dean, for he was a dean, no less. And
with that he was off through a discourse on Latin
roots it would have deaved you to hear.

The wee gnome bade him good-day, not a whit
the wiser, and stopped next at a poor woman's
door.

" A blessing on the house ! " says he. " And
could you tell me, ma'am, where I would find
heartsease ? "

The good-wife scattered hens and weans from
under her feet and wrung her hands from the suds
of a week's washing before she made answer.

" Would you seek it here ? " she scolded. " And
me with six children in tatters and hardly the price
of a herring between them and starvation ! Sure
heart's ease is a thing I never knew since the day
I was married on a drunken sailor, and if that's
your quest you have further to go ! "

The gnome went on at that and overtook a
white-haired grannie teaching a two-year-old its
first tottering steps.

" Did I ever happen on heart's ease ? " says she.
" Well, indeed then, I did. For after my man
was snatched from me I shut myself away and
vowed to be done with the world and its troubles.
But feth I was near killed with loneliness. Better

love than heart's ease, if one might be choosing, and a stepping out with each generation until God gives you rest."

So he wandered and wandered up hill and down dale, and at the end of his quest came on a quiet woman clearing her flower border in the cool of the evening. It was autumn-time, with her dahlias and marigolds flaunting bright heads, and about her was a riot of late roses and Michaelmas daisies.

She dropped her trowel when the wee gnome paused

" Does there grow in your garden the plant called heartsease? "

at her gate and smiled with her eyes in a nice way that she had.

"Content speed the work!" said he. "And does there grow in your garden the plant called heartsease?"

[136]

" There does," she said, " for I found it here and it roots itself year in year out; though there isn't a flower to be showing you till they return with the spring. But haven't I seeds I can give you —and let you sow them and raise up heartsease for yourself."

She hurried away to the house with that and tipping some round, dried, seeds from an old china cup brought them to him in a screw of paper. Wishing him good luck and sending him from her rejoicing.

Away he went, home to his island, and nearly the first person he saw on arrival was the distressful damsel—and her wreathed in smiles and treading on air.

" Heart's ease!" says she. " Och, my wee man, sure I have it this minute. Isn't my true love back from the sea and the two of us to be married the morrow's morn! But plant your small seeds since I have no use for them and see does there grow up a flower sweet as my joy."

And he did . . . And there bloomed in his garden shy velvet blossoms. Five heart-shaped petals each one had, golden as sunshine and rayed with blue. The scent of honey went with them and the gladness of God, and the sight of them was fit to soften men's sorrow.

[137]

In the gnome's hid pleasance they bloom to this day, though they have grown wild and small for want of his care. Some call them pansies, but the country name for them is 'heartsease' the wide world over.

THE ROADMENDER'S COAT

ALL the children loved Barney, the roadsman. And if he had up with a magic flute not a wean in Portavogie—or for miles beyond—but would have followed the tattered skirts of his coat, and him dancing them away through a cleft in the hills or the secret portals of Tir nan Og.

His coat was nearly as great a favourite as himself—being of some old outlandish cut and ornamented with five large brass buttons, three in the front and two at the rear, above the swallow-tails. He had it off Squire Dillon, a great sporting gentleman of his day, and the original colour was a bright bottle-green, though betwixt stains and patches it had been well toned by time. Once it had boasted a fine velvet collar, and shreds of the plush still clung like a streaking of bright moss on the dank fall of a thatch; while here and there was a frogging or worn remnant of braid. But in the great flapped pockets lay its whole charm! You never knew what Barney might not produce from his pockets. Cob-nuts and candy and gay bunches of feathers for the making of fish-hooks. Pop-guns that shot out round lengths of seaweed. Tops and boats and hickory whistles; and small chairs carved from conkers for the fascination of ladies.

There was never in the world such a wizard as Barney!

And in the tail pocket of his coat Barney kept his magic handkerchief. It seemed just an ordinary square of red cotton with a sprinkled pattern of blue and yellow dots, such as one might purchase from any huckster for a penny; but Barney said he had found it on a fairy rath, and at Barney's touch it became endowed with pixie powers! If you looked for it in his hat it would be sighted slyly peeping from the depth of his cuff. And should you watch Barney, with your own two eyes, safely fold and cover it with his largest flint—hey pass there it was in his brogue, and Barney rubbing his grizzled poll in wonder-

ment at such antics. While only for Barney
would it go through its skavies!

Children travelled far out of their way on their
journeys from school in order to pass the heap of
stones by ditch or cross-roads where Barney sat
perched on his bundle of sacks, merrily whistling
and hammering his flints. And ofttimes they
clambered through hedges or from behind a stone
wall to come on him suddenly and take him by
surprise, tweaking his old coat and clinging about
him like so many bright elves conjured up at his
call.

There were never such stories as those Barney
could tell, for he had been away to the wars and
to far distant lands; or such rollicking songs
as Barney would sing with the clink of his
hammer to mark the refrains: Lanty Leary and
Craigbilly Fair, and The Ould Man of Killyburn
Brae:

> There was an old man down Killyburn Brae,
> Right fol, right fol, tilly fol ay,
> There was an ould man down at Killyburn Brae
> Had a scouldin' ould wife for the most of his day,
> With a right fol da doll, tilly fol lol,
> Fol de da doll de, doll de da day.

Barney had no wife, nor any belonging to him,
and the children made up stories about where he

lived and how he fared, though Barney said he consorted with fairies and feasted with them off corn-brose and cockles! In truth he had no settled abode, but moved from place to place as his work took him—his couch being often a pile of sail-cloth or dry hantle of nets in some fisherman's shed; while he was dependent on the kindly service of strangers for his food and his comforts.

One bleak November evening Barney ceased work at dusk and took the shore road home to his lodging. The sun had gone down like a fiery ball and a thin dank mist had risen, shrouding the sea and the sullen sky. The bare thorns and whin bushes were hung with moist webs, and above the restless sough of the waves the mewing of the gulls came drifting eerily.

Near a rough stretch of dune grass on the slope of the sea-bank lay two or three upturned boats and a clutter of lobster pots, and as Barney approached one of the crawls dropped legs from under it and went leaping and jigging out over the hummocks like some worricow's chariot.

Thinking that maybe a stray sea-bird had been captured and caged, Barney left down his tools and set chase after the crawl to bring it to a standstill. But on peering through the rods didn't he

spy a very small man in a green guernsey and
red cap, and him clawing and jumping and tear-
ing with rage.

"Let me out, let me out," screeched the wee
man. "Will you quit staring there like a gomeril
and render assistance. Don't you see me here
catched and caged, and must you be as unhandy
as you are ill-looking?"

"Houl' on, houl' on!" says Barney, soothing
him, and minded to let him cool a bit before
releasing him from his predicament—if only to
teach him to keep a civil tongue in his head.
"How did you get in there at all—and is it you
is responsible for the shortage of crayfish and
depredations in the catches hereabouts?" And
with that Barney lifted the lobster pot clumsily
so the wee man stood on his head with his legs
waving up in the air—helpless as a wasp in a jar
full of jam.

The angry wee gnome spluttered and choked
and seemed as if he might take some kind of a
fit, being so beside himself with rage. And when
Barney, at last, loosed his breeches where they
had hanked on a spike and pulled him out
through the opening in the crawl, he just stamped
and yammered—and then, jouking down, would
have slipped past Barney and made good his

escape, only that Barney grasped him round the middle and swung him aloft.

"Hi! Not so fast," admonished Barney. "Have you no manners about you at all, and you under an obligation? By rights I should be demanding that you grant me a wish in the place of a gratuity, but I misdoubt you must be at variance with your own kith and kin—since it seems you hadn't what magic would free you from bondage."

The fairy-man gave a growl at that and wriggled himself round in Barney's big hands.

"Let me down," says he, with a cackle of laughter, "and watch have I magic enough for my needs!"

And at the spiteful glint in his eye Barney started to stuff him back into his cage, being dubious of his good intentions and suddenly taking a distaste for his company.

But when the wee man perceived that Barney was in earnest and fully intended to leave him a prisoner, he changed his tactics, and the long and the short of it came to be that he offered Barney a wish in exchange for his freedom.

Barney stipulated that it must be a good wish —and he thought long and hard as to what he should ask.

"By the looks of you," remarked the saucy wee man, "you could be doing with the present of a new coat this minute." And at that Barney slapped his thigh in great delight.

"The very thing," says he, "and see to it now that the cut is stylish and the frieze hard-wearing. I have managed half my life-time with the one I have on—and feth a brand-new garment should do me my day.

"Produce your dress-coat," decides Barney— and looked round as if he expected to see it fall on him from the air.

"Troth, and I am no tailor," said the fairy-man, perched now on the top of the creel, "but I have a friend I might prevail on to sew your long seams. He will be wanting your measurements and for you to choose your own cut and style—so come back here on this day week and we'll see then what can be done."

With that he slid down and dissolved into the mist; and Barney went whistling on his way— half-minded, when he came to think it over, that he had dreamed the whole affair.

But on a week to the very day didn't the fairy-man reappear—and with him a wizened wee imp with a yardstick and a goose and a long pair of shears. He had horn-rimmed spectacles perched on his nose and a rounded cap set on the back of his head. About his neck hung a thick plaited skein of grey yarn; and the front of his jerkin was studded with needles and pins. And he was bent double beneath a ponderous roll of stout frieze.

He had horn-rimmed spectacles perched on his nose

He ordered Barney to jouk down on his hunkers; and he measured and snipped, and danced round and round intent on his work —so that before Barney had recovered from his astonishment wasn't he fitted up with a brand-new stylish coat. Cut, sewn, pressed, and complete to the last button.

[146]

"Fold up the old one and we may as well take it with us," said the first little rogue. "Sure a fine gentleman like yourself can have no further use for such tatters." But though they wheedled and coaxed, and then gave him abuse, and even tried to take it by force—Barney steadfastly refused to part with his old coat. So that in the end the two tricksters retired defeated—leaving Barney to pursue his way, proud in the snug new frieze, with his ragged old friend tucked under his arm.

Now whether it was the pinching and pushing he had suffered in the affray, or the heat of the argument with the two rascallions, Barney couldn't decide; but the fact remained that from then until bedtime he found himself in a very bad temper. He slept peaceably enough; but he was no sooner dressed in the morning than his ill-humour returned to him threefold—so that he could have eaten the face off the first one that caused him annoyance.

He had always been kindly and easy-going, but now he grew morose and quarrelsome and apt to make the worst of every trifling vexation. His old dog, that had been used to lie close to his elbow or curled up on his coat if he worked in shirt-sleeves, would slink away into the ditch and watch him warily from a distance, as though un-

[147]

certain and timid of incurring his displeasure.

While if the children stopped by his pitch he chased them with frowns. For the pockets of the new coat were too small and close to hold cobnuts or candy—and he had no patience to spare for the making of toys.

Soon it came to be recognized that Barney was greatly changed. People missed his cheery whistle as he travelled the roads or sat cracking his flints. And as time went on they began to avoid him and to leave him to his own devices, since they only got a curt nod in reply to their greeting—and he had grown so dour and prone to swift angers. He found himself shunning men's company; and would slouch along not wishing to be seen. And there was no laughter in him now, nor joy in simple things. And the world, that had seemed a kindly place, was on a sudden become cold and drear. While in the sore heart of him was a puzzlement and a lonesomeness. For he would grope in his own mind wondering what ailed him, and strive to attribute to this cause or that his fretfulness and his discontent.

So the winter passed. And on a spring morning, with the sun burning down from a clear sky, Barney saw fit to discard his new coat.

It seemed with its removal that in some strange

THE ROADMENDER'S COAT
Barney set chase after the crawl

way the sunshine grew brighter and the song of
the little green linnets more joyous. And before
Barney was aware he found himself smiling and
chanting in unison.

" Fol de da day," sang Barney, and the old dog
came bounding to nuzzle his hand. While a wee
girleen, passing by on her way to school, drew
near at his call and watched his red handkerchief
go through its performance.

Barney had never thought to connect his
change of heart with the loss of his old coat; but
now he. looked long and hard at the fairy-frieze.
He tried it out just to satisfy himself; putting it
on and taking it off, and marking how the day
clouded or grew bright as his spirits rose or fell.
Trailing it behind him through a ploughed field
he made to drape it round a scarecrow that stood
whipped and blown in the sudden scurry of a
shower. Then, fearing that the land-owner might
notice and raise questions, he carried it away and
left it lying by the twisted root of a thorn bush,
in hopes that the lurking fairy-folk would find and
dispose of it.

But later, growing uneasy, he recovered it
again, and having tied it up tightly, weighted the
bundle with the largest granite slab to be found
in his tip. And going home at nightfall he took

and threw it into the nearest dyke, and saw it sink deep down amongst the green slime and the rushes.

And he stayed to watch until the troubled water was still and the bull-frogs had resumed their croaking.

He made to drape it round a scarecrow

It was remarked that Barney discarded his fine frieze and ever after remained faithful to his old swallow-tail. But in answer to all inquiries he would avow his preference for a loose-fitting and stress the convenience and depth of the pockets!

Soon the children had welcomed the return of

[150]

their lost playmate and once more the weans of Portavogie scampered at his heels.

"Barney, dear Barney," they would coax, "tell us the tale of the fairy-frieze." But Barney maintained that the whole wonder of the story was bound up in his patches, and that the magic lay hid in the measure of his content.

He never again asked to replace his old coat. And, indeed, it lasted him out, bravely, for the rest of his lifetime.

THE QUICKEN TREE

MARY MCANALLY had cried all night with the toothache, and in the morning her granny bade her go away and stick a pin in the quicken tree and wish herself well rid of the pain.

The quicken tree grew beside the old Round Tower and its bark was all pricked with pins, for as well as having a charm against the face-ache it could grant you the wish of your heart or be sending to you the lover of your dreams. A fairy thorn it was, and as old as, or older than, the Round Tower.

Mary McAnally passed down between the swaying meadow grasses hoping that she would not meet with anyone or be questioned about her errand. Her granny was wise, but sometimes when she told things that her granny believed

[152]

in the younger folk of the village would laugh. Still and all the country people treated her granny with great respect, and set a store by her strange wisdom. She never left her little house on the hill, but farmers brought her the sick cows and she made them well, and she was learned in the use of the herbs that grew in their white-walled garden plot.

Mary McAnally stuck her pin in the fairy thorn and wished her wish. The sun made a pleasant warmth and it seemed that the pain in her tooth was less.

She seated herself contentedly on the green bank that sloped down from the Round Tower and, shading her eyes, saw far away the long range of the Wicklow hills rising up into the sky. In a year from now she would have left school, and she supposed she would go up to the big farm beyont to work for Mrs. Casey. She had had a notion that she would like to learn the dressmaking, for her teacher said she was clever with her needle; but if her granny wouldn't go with her to the town she couldn't be leaving her. Maybe when you had lived all your life with the hills around you, you mightn't take kindly to the close streets of a town. And it was lovely in her granny's garden in springtime, when the flowering currant bush waved against the window and the daffydowndillies shone gold in the borders.

A blue mist folded the mountains out of sight and Mary McAnally stayed sunk in dreams. It might have been that she slept, for when she roused there was a song in the air and a ring of wee, green-clad people, holding hands together, stretched to encompass herself and the quicken tree.

"Mary," they sang, "Mary McAnally, will you be telling us now the desire of your heart."

She pushed back the hair from her eyes and took them all in with a wondering look before she made answer.

"Sure it's what I don't know," she sighed, "and me sticking pins in the quicken tree and hoping to be granted wee everyday requests. If it's a big wish I am to be given, what shall it be?"

"What shall it be?" echoed the fairy people. "Let you be telling us, Mary McAnally, the wish that lies nearest to your heart."

"It would take me a day-and-a-half to tell you the thoughts that come into my head," Mary McAnally confided in perplexity. "I'm not taking overly to poverty and hard work, but if I got things too nice and easy it might happen that I'd find myself growing stony-hearted. I

[154]

could be asking for contentment: my granny
wouldn't change places with the Queen on her
throne and she envies no woman that walks the
earth, even though we'd often times go hungry

"Choose, choose," urged the fairy people

and cold. It's hard, so it is, for a body to be
choosing."

"Choose, choose," urged the fairy people, and
a blackbird perched high in the quicken tree out-
rivalled and outsang them.

"There's Mrs. Casey, now," pondered Mary

[155]

McAnally, " with two servant girls and a silk dress for Sundays. But whenever I go for a can of milk she's scolding and fretting; and she sits heavy by the fire and isn't as nimble on her feet as my granny. She'll chase wee childer away from her door, whereas my granny took me in when my own ones died, and she wouldn't be parting with me for a crock of gold. Och, love's the kindliest and best thing of all. A loving heart is the gift I'll be choosing."

The wee folk had vanished, but the blackbird was still singing. High and clear from the quicken tree he sounded his song, fearless and beautiful, and Mary McAnally scrambled to her feet. Her toothache was gone and happiness touched her. She pricked the quicken tree a second time and recorded trustfully the desire of her heart.

THE ELF-RIDDEN PIG

THERE wasn't in the length and breadth of Ireland, nor in the entire county of Roscommon, the like of the Widow O'Riordan's lovely fat pig.

She had it off Farmer Sweedlepipe as a dilling, just a wee pink porker that was one too many for the old sow, and nobody—least of all Farmer Sweedlepipe—expected it to be making the best of things in the way that it did.

Farmer Sweedlepipe never stinted his trough-food, whilst the Widow O'Riordan's pet pig only saw the scraps she collected from her neighbours, with the leavings of her own potato crop and a wee swill of skim milk now and again, so it was hard to account for the fact that it grew to be

[157]

the wonder and envy of the district, and had its brothers and sisters beaten to nothing.

It was of a placid disposition—rootling about the lanes contentedly with a length of rope tied to its leg when the Widow O'Riordan took it out walking, as she did every day—and her with a blue worsted stocking on the pins, waiting complacently for the complimentary remarks of the passers-by.

" That's a fine fat pig," people would say.

" Och aye," the Widow O'Riordan answered modestly. " A good wee crathur of a pig that has contrived to nourish itself on potato parings. I am told I should enter it at the Ballaghadereen show."

Farmer Sweedlepipe made an offer to buy it back at a good price, and the dealers were never off her doorstep, but the Widow O'Riordan couldn't bring herself to be parting with her pet.

Silas, she named the pig after the Farmer Sweedlepipe himself, and Silas grew and thrived until he was just an amazement to see.

His craw—or pigsty—was built on to the end of the Widow O'Riordan's little thatched cottage, and from the time she closed Silas up after his supper to the time when she let him out for his breakfast, he never made a muff. Until one

[158]

moonlit night about twelve of the clock, when she was awakened by an unearthly squealing that brought her bolt upright in bed, and on to the floor in a couple of hops.

"My pig!" says she. "Lamenty oh, some rascal is after my darlin' pig, and me left without man or gun at the mercy of robbers!" And she threw her shawl about her and opened the house door to gleek and see what was afoot.

A tawny owl hooted from a hollow tree over the road, and white moonshine made everything as clear as day, but the squealing had stopped and there was nothing to be seen.

With her heart in her mouth she crept quietly to the sty, and the hasp on the door was just as she had left it, and the peg of wood in place to be keeping it secure. It was when she made closer inspection that she discovered her loss. There was the flattened straw where Silas had lain, but Silas himself had been stolen away.

Not another wink of sleep did the poor woman get, and her only waiting for daylight, to be starting the hue and cry. Soon after dawn she kindled her fire and boiled the kettle, and she had just comforted herself with a mouthful of tea when she heard a grunting and a pushing at the half-docr, and into the kitchen tottered Silas the pig.

[159]

A sad and sorry sight he was, and a queer-looking pickle, and him blinking his small eyes as though he was donsie, and clabbered all up his four fat legs with a black coating of bog mud. The Widow O'Riordan screeched when she saw him, but she was more than happy to have him back. "Come in, avick," says she. "Sure don't I know you must have given the rogues who stole you the slip, and you with the right good sense. But you're done out entirely. Rest you now, and I'll go away to purchase a padlock that'll be putting thieves from the like of this night's work."

The widow screwed a padlock on the door of the sty, and laid herself down that night satisfied that any further attempt at pig-stealing had been frustrated. But when twelve o'clock struck the squealing rose again—and though the padlock had not been touched Silas was missing and away until daybreak.

"My-a-my," said the Widow O'Riordan. "What's this at all?"

Next night she settled herself under an ash tree that grew near the gable end of her house and waited expectantly for the moon to rise.

Prompt on the stroke of twelve by the church clock shadows started flitting about the sty, and before the tawny owl had hooted twice out

[160]

through the mysteriously opened door came Silas,
dragged by the tail, with three brown elves hanging on, and another two riding him straddle-
legged. Away they went down the boreen that
led to the bog-place, with their peeled sally rods

Their peeled sally rods thrashing and flailing the poor pig's sides

thrashing and flailing the poor pig's sides, and
him squealing melia murder and raising hulla-
baloo.

The same thing happened every night while the
moon was at the full, and each morning at daybreak Silas reappeared, chap-fallen and bog-
mired, and done out entirely.

Silas started to get thin, and so did the widow

[161]

—for there didn't seem any notoriety before her once sonsy pet only to be sold for streaky bacon. All his pink chubbiness was gone, his fine curly tail hung straight as a yard of pump water, and a dirtier or more commonplace little pig you couldn't be finding.

It was a heart-scald, so it was, and before the next full moon the Widow O'Riordan set off with a print of butter and an offering of hen's eggs, to lay the whole case before the Wise Woman.

And as an outcome of the visit she made her own plans.

With the full of the moon the brown elves were at their pranks again; and when the Widow O'Riordan got them away riding poor Silas, she dragged forth the pig-trough and set it across the boreen, filled to the brim with sludge water from the ditch. Then she took her clothes-line and knotted it from tree to tree at a certain height. And after that she stationed herself beneath the shelter of the mountain ash, the way she would be kept safe from enchantment, and waited slyly on events.

As the first streaks of dawn appeared she heard the pig squealing in the distance, and soon it hove in sight, galloping its best, with the elves hanging on to ears and tail, and them in helpless kinks of laughter.

Silas, coming helter-skelter, jumped the trough in fine style, but the slung cord caught the brown elves, and tumbled them backwards into the sludge water as neatly as you'd be flicking bannocks from a griddle. The Widow O'Riordan chuckled, and when the elves had picked themselves out of the trough they made away over the fields as hard as they could go, and that was the last she, or Silas ever heard tell of them.

Silas fattened up again in no time, and won first prize, and wore a blue rosette at the Ballaghadereen show.

The Widow O'Riordan kept a close tongue about the elf-riding. She made a sugar-cake and left it within the pixie-ring to placate the brown elves; and they didn't take amiss the wee trick she had played on them.

[163]

And for the hardness of men's hearts
The wee folk went from us.

(Old Irish Legend.)

The fairies went from the world, dear,
  Because men's hearts grew cold;
And only the eyes of children see
  What is hidden from the old;
And only the magic of love, dear,
  Can ever turn the key
That unlocks the gates of Fairyland
  To set the wee folk free.

Printed for the Publishers by Butler & Tanner Ltd., Frome and London
194.1066